www.EffortlessMath.com

... So Much More Online!

✓ FREE Math lessons

✓ More Math learning books!

✓ Mathematics Worksheets

✓ Online Math Tutors

Need a PDF version of this book?

Please visit www.EffortlessMath.com

STAAR Grade 8

Math Workbook

2020 - 2021

The Most Comprehensive Review for the Math Section of the STAAR Grade 8 Test

By

Reza Nazari & Ava Ross

All inquiries should be addressed to:

info@effortlessMath.com

www.EffortlessMath.com

ISBN: 978-1-64612-329-2

Published by: Effortless Math Education

www.EffortlessMath.com

Visit www.EffortlessMath.com

for Online Math Practice

Description

STAAR Grade 8 Math Workbook 2020 – 2021, which reflects the 2020 – 2021 test guidelines and topics, provides students with the confidence and math skills they need to succeed on the STAAR Math, offering a solid foundation of basic Math topics with abundant exercises for each topic. It is designed to address the needs of STAAR test takers who must have a working knowledge of basic Math.

This comprehensive workbook with over 2,500 sample questions and 2 full-length STAAR Math tests is all you need to fully prepare for the STAAR Math. It will help you learn everything you need to ace the math section of the STAAR test.

This STAAR Math workbook's new edition has been updated to replicate questions appearing on the most recent STAAR math tests. Upon completion of this workbook, you will have a solid foundation and sufficient practice to ace the STAAR Math test. **This workbook is your ticket to scoring higher on STAAR Grade 8 Math.**

Inside the pages of this comprehensive STAAR Math workbook, you can learn basic math operations in a structured manner with a complete study program to help you understand essential math skills. It also has many exciting features, including:

- ✓ Content 100% aligned with the 2020 STAAR ® test
- ✓ Written by STAAR ® Math tutors and test experts
- ✓ Complete coverage of all STAAR Math concepts and topics which you will be tested
- ✓ Over 2,500 additional STAAR math practice questions in both multiple-choice and grid-in formats with answers grouped by topic, so you can focus on your weak areas
- ✓ Abundant Math skill building exercises to help test-takers approach different question types that might be unfamiliar to them
- ✓ Exercises on different STAAR Math topics such as integers, percent, equations, polynomials, exponents and radicals
- ✓ 2 full-length practice tests (featuring new question types) with detailed answers

This STAAR Math Workbook and other Effortless Math Education books are used by thousands of students each year to help them review core content areas, brush-up in math, discover their strengths and weaknesses, and achieve their best scores on the STAAR test.

Contents

Simplifying Fractions

✍ *Simplify each fraction.*

1) $\frac{10}{15} =$

2) $\frac{8}{20} =$

3) $\frac{12}{42} =$

4) $\frac{5}{20} =$

5) $\frac{6}{18} =$

6) $\frac{18}{27} =$

7) $\frac{15}{55} =$

8) $\frac{24}{54} =$

9) $\frac{63}{72} =$

10) $\frac{40}{64} =$

11) $\frac{23}{46} =$

12) $\frac{35}{63} =$

13) $\frac{32}{36} =$

14) $\frac{81}{99} =$

15) $\frac{16}{64} =$

16) $\frac{14}{35} =$

17) $\frac{19}{38}$

18) $\frac{18}{54} =$

19) $\frac{56}{70} =$

20) $\frac{40}{45} =$

21) $\frac{9}{90} =$

22) $\frac{20}{25} =$

23) $\frac{32}{48} =$

24) $\frac{7}{49} =$

25) $\frac{18}{48} =$

26) $\frac{54}{108} =$

Homework: #.....

Simplifying Fractions - Answers

✎ Simplify each fraction.

1) $\dfrac{10}{15} = \dfrac{2}{3}$

2) $\dfrac{8}{20} = \dfrac{2}{5}$

3) $\dfrac{12}{42} = \dfrac{2}{7}$

4) $\dfrac{5}{20} = \dfrac{1}{4}$

5) $\dfrac{6}{18} = \dfrac{1}{3}$

6) $\dfrac{18}{27} = \dfrac{2}{3}$

7) $\dfrac{15}{55} = \dfrac{3}{11}$

8) $\dfrac{24}{54} = \dfrac{4}{9}$

9) $\dfrac{63}{72} = \dfrac{7}{8}$

10) $\dfrac{40}{64} = \dfrac{5}{8}$

11) $\dfrac{23}{46} = \dfrac{1}{2}$

12) $\dfrac{35}{63} = \dfrac{5}{9}$

13) $\dfrac{32}{36} = \dfrac{8}{9}$

14) $\dfrac{81}{99} = \dfrac{9}{11}$

15) $\dfrac{16}{64} = \dfrac{1}{4}$

16) $\dfrac{14}{35} = \dfrac{2}{5}$

17) $\dfrac{19}{38} = \dfrac{1}{2}$

18) $\dfrac{18}{54} = \dfrac{1}{3}$

19) $\dfrac{56}{70} = \dfrac{4}{5}$

20) $\dfrac{40}{45} = \dfrac{8}{9}$

21) $\dfrac{9}{90} = \dfrac{1}{10}$

22) $\dfrac{20}{25} = \dfrac{4}{5}$

23) $\dfrac{32}{48} = \dfrac{2}{3}$

24) $\dfrac{7}{49} = \dfrac{1}{7}$

25) $\dfrac{18}{48} = \dfrac{3}{8}$

26) $\dfrac{54}{108} = \dfrac{1}{2}$

Homework: #.....

Adding and Subtracting Fractions

✎ *Calculate and write the answer in lowest term.*

1) $\frac{1}{5} + \frac{1}{7} =$

2) $\frac{3}{7} + \frac{4}{5} =$

3) $\frac{3}{8} - \frac{1}{9} =$

4) $\frac{4}{5} - \frac{5}{9} =$

5) $\frac{2}{9} + \frac{1}{3} =$

6) $\frac{3}{10} + \frac{2}{5} =$

7) $\frac{9}{10} - \frac{4}{5} =$

8) $\frac{7}{9} - \frac{3}{7} =$

9) $\frac{3}{4} + \frac{1}{3} =$

10) $\frac{3}{8} + \frac{2}{5} =$

11) $\frac{3}{4} - \frac{2}{5} =$

12) $\frac{7}{9} - \frac{2}{3} =$

13) $\frac{4}{9} + \frac{5}{6} =$

14) $\frac{2}{3} + \frac{1}{4} =$

15) $\frac{9}{10} - \frac{3}{5} =$

16) $\frac{7}{12} - \frac{1}{2} =$

17) $\frac{4}{5} + \frac{2}{3} =$

18) $\frac{5}{7} + \frac{1}{5} =$

19) $\frac{5}{9} - \frac{2}{5} =$

20) $\frac{3}{5} - \frac{2}{9} =$

21) $\frac{7}{9} + \frac{1}{7} =$

22) $\frac{5}{8} + \frac{2}{3} =$

23) $\frac{4}{7} + \frac{2}{3} =$

24) $\frac{6}{7} - \frac{4}{9} =$

25) $\frac{4}{5} - \frac{2}{15} =$

26) $\frac{2}{9} + \frac{4}{5} =$

Adding and Subtracting Fractions - Answers

✎ *Calculate and write the answer in lowest term.*

1) $\frac{1}{5} + \frac{1}{7} = \frac{12}{35}$

2) $\frac{3}{7} + \frac{4}{5} = \frac{43}{35}$

3) $\frac{3}{8} - \frac{1}{9} = \frac{19}{72}$

4) $\frac{4}{5} - \frac{5}{9} = \frac{11}{45}$

5) $\frac{2}{9} + \frac{1}{3} = \frac{5}{9}$

6) $\frac{3}{10} + \frac{2}{5} = \frac{7}{10}$

7) $\frac{9}{10} - \frac{4}{5} = \frac{1}{10}$

8) $\frac{7}{9} - \frac{3}{7} = \frac{22}{63}$

9) $\frac{3}{4} + \frac{1}{3} = \frac{13}{12}$

10) $\frac{3}{8} + \frac{2}{5} = \frac{31}{40}$

11) $\frac{3}{4} - \frac{2}{5} = \frac{7}{20}$

12) $\frac{7}{9} - \frac{2}{3} = \frac{1}{9}$

13) $\frac{4}{9} + \frac{5}{6} = \frac{23}{18}$

14) $\frac{2}{3} + \frac{1}{4} = \frac{11}{12}$

15) $\frac{9}{10} - \frac{3}{5} = \frac{3}{10}$

16) $\frac{7}{12} - \frac{1}{2} = \frac{1}{12}$

17) $\frac{4}{5} + \frac{2}{3} = \frac{22}{15}$

18) $\frac{5}{7} + \frac{1}{5} = \frac{32}{35}$

19) $\frac{5}{9} - \frac{2}{5} = \frac{7}{45}$

20) $\frac{3}{5} - \frac{2}{9} = \frac{17}{45}$

21) $\frac{7}{9} + \frac{1}{7} = \frac{58}{63}$

22) $\frac{5}{8} + \frac{2}{3} = \frac{31}{24}$

23) $\frac{4}{7} + \frac{2}{3} = \frac{26}{21}$

24) $\frac{6}{7} - \frac{4}{9} = \frac{26}{63}$

25) $\frac{4}{5} - \frac{2}{15} = \frac{2}{3}$

26) $\frac{2}{9} + \frac{4}{5} = \frac{46}{45}$

Multiplying and Dividing Fractions

✍ *Solve and write the answer in lowest term.*

1) $\frac{1}{2} \times \frac{4}{5} =$

2) $\frac{1}{5} \times \frac{6}{7} =$

3) $\frac{1}{3} \div \frac{1}{7} =$

4) $\frac{1}{7} \div \frac{3}{8} =$

5) $\frac{2}{3} \times \frac{4}{7} =$

6) $\frac{5}{7} \times \frac{3}{4} =$

7) $\frac{2}{5} \div \frac{3}{7} =$

8) $\frac{3}{7} \div \frac{5}{8} =$

9) $\frac{3}{8} \times \frac{4}{7} =$

10) $\frac{2}{9} \times \frac{6}{11} =$

11) $\frac{1}{10} \div \frac{3}{8} =$

12) $\frac{3}{10} \div \frac{4}{5} =$

13) $\frac{6}{7} \times \frac{4}{9} =$

14) $\frac{3}{7} \times \frac{5}{6} =$

15) $\frac{7}{9} \div \frac{6}{11} =$

16) $\frac{1}{15} \div \frac{2}{3} =$

17) $\frac{1}{13} \times \frac{1}{2} =$

18) $\frac{1}{12} \times \frac{4}{7} =$

19) $\frac{1}{15} \div \frac{4}{9} =$

20) $\frac{1}{16} \div \frac{1}{2} =$

21) $\frac{4}{7} \times \frac{5}{8} =$

22) $\frac{1}{11} \times \frac{4}{5} =$

23) $\frac{1}{18} \div \frac{5}{6} =$

24) $\frac{1}{15} \div \frac{3}{8} =$

25) $\frac{1}{11} \times \frac{3}{4} =$

26) $\frac{1}{14} \times \frac{2}{3} =$

Multiplying and Dividing Fractions - Answers

✎ *Solve and write the answer in lowest term.*

1) $\frac{1}{2} \times \frac{4}{5} = \frac{2}{5}$

2) $\frac{1}{5} \times \frac{6}{7} = \frac{6}{35}$

3) $\frac{1}{3} \div \frac{1}{7} = \frac{7}{3}$

4) $\frac{1}{7} \div \frac{3}{8} = \frac{8}{21}$

5) $\frac{2}{3} \times \frac{4}{7} = \frac{8}{21}$

6) $\frac{5}{7} \times \frac{3}{4} = \frac{15}{28}$

7) $\frac{2}{5} \div \frac{3}{7} = \frac{14}{15}$

8) $\frac{3}{7} \div \frac{5}{8} = \frac{24}{35}$

9) $\frac{3}{8} \times \frac{4}{7} = \frac{3}{14}$

10) $\frac{2}{9} \times \frac{6}{11} = \frac{4}{33}$

11) $\frac{1}{10} \div \frac{3}{8} = \frac{4}{15}$

12) $\frac{3}{10} \div \frac{4}{5} = \frac{3}{8}$

13) $\frac{6}{7} \times \frac{4}{9} = \frac{8}{21}$

14) $\frac{3}{7} \times \frac{5}{6} = \frac{5}{14}$

15) $\frac{7}{9} \div \frac{6}{11} = \frac{77}{54}$

16) $\frac{1}{15} \div \frac{2}{3} = \frac{1}{10}$

17) $\frac{1}{13} \times \frac{1}{2} = \frac{1}{26}$

18) $\frac{1}{12} \times \frac{4}{7} = \frac{1}{21}$

19) $\frac{1}{15} \div \frac{4}{9} = \frac{3}{20}$

20) $\frac{1}{16} \div \frac{1}{2} = \frac{1}{8}$

21) $\frac{4}{7} \times \frac{5}{8} = \frac{5}{14}$

22) $\frac{1}{11} \times \frac{4}{5} = \frac{4}{55}$

23) $\frac{1}{18} \div \frac{5}{6} = \frac{1}{15}$

24) $\frac{1}{15} \div \frac{3}{8} = \frac{8}{45}$

25) $\frac{1}{11} \times \frac{3}{4} = \frac{3}{44}$

26) $\frac{1}{14} \times \frac{2}{3} = \frac{1}{21}$

Homework: #.....

Adding Mixed Numbers

✎ *Solve and write the answer in lowest terms.*

1) $3\frac{1}{5} + 2\frac{2}{9} =$

2) $1\frac{1}{7} + 5\frac{2}{5} =$

3) $4\frac{4}{5} + 1\frac{2}{7} =$

4) $2\frac{4}{7} + 2\frac{3}{5} =$

5) $1\frac{5}{6} + 1\frac{2}{5} =$

6) $3\frac{5}{7} + 1\frac{2}{9} =$

7) $3\frac{5}{8} + 2\frac{1}{3} =$

8) $1\frac{6}{7} + 3\frac{2}{9} =$

9) $2\frac{5}{9} + 1\frac{1}{4} =$

10) $3\frac{7}{9} + 2\frac{5}{6} =$

11) $2\frac{1}{10} + 2\frac{2}{5} =$

12) $1\frac{3}{10} + 3\frac{4}{5} =$

13) $3\frac{1}{12} + 2\frac{1}{3} =$

14) $5\frac{1}{11} + 1\frac{1}{2} =$

15) $3\frac{1}{21} + 2\frac{2}{3} =$

16) $4\frac{1}{24} + 1\frac{5}{8} =$

17) $2\frac{1}{25} + 3\frac{3}{5} =$

18) $3\frac{1}{15} + 2\frac{2}{10} =$

19) $5\frac{6}{7} + 2\frac{1}{3} =$

20) $2\frac{1}{8} + 3\frac{3}{4} =$

21) $2\frac{5}{7} + 2\frac{2}{21} =$

22) $4\frac{1}{6} + 1\frac{4}{5} =$

23) $3\frac{5}{6} + 1\frac{2}{7} =$

24) $2\frac{7}{8} + 3\frac{1}{3} =$

25) $3\frac{1}{17} + 1\frac{1}{2} =$

26) $1\frac{1}{18} + 1\frac{4}{9} =$

Adding Mixed Numbers - Answers

✎ *Solve and write the answer in lowest terms.*

1) $3\frac{1}{5} + 2\frac{2}{9} = 5\frac{19}{45}$

2) $1\frac{1}{7} + 5\frac{2}{5} = 6\frac{19}{35}$

3) $4\frac{4}{5} + 1\frac{2}{7} = 6\frac{3}{35}$

4) $2\frac{4}{7} + 2\frac{3}{5} = 5\frac{6}{35}$

5) $1\frac{5}{6} + 1\frac{2}{5} = 3\frac{7}{30}$

6) $3\frac{5}{7} + 1\frac{2}{9} = 4\frac{59}{63}$

7) $3\frac{5}{8} + 2\frac{1}{3} = 5\frac{23}{24}$

8) $1\frac{6}{7} + 3\frac{2}{9} = 5\frac{5}{63}$

9) $2\frac{5}{9} + 1\frac{1}{4} = 3\frac{29}{36}$

10) $3\frac{7}{9} + 2\frac{5}{6} = 6\frac{11}{18}$

11) $2\frac{1}{10} + 2\frac{2}{5} = 4\frac{1}{2}$

12) $1\frac{3}{10} + 3\frac{4}{5} = 5\frac{1}{10}$

13) $3\frac{1}{12} + 2\frac{1}{3} = 5\frac{5}{12}$

14) $5\frac{1}{11} + 1\frac{1}{2} = 6\frac{13}{22}$

15) $3\frac{1}{21} + 2\frac{2}{3} = 5\frac{5}{7}$

16) $4\frac{1}{24} + 1\frac{5}{8} = 5\frac{2}{3}$

17) $2\frac{1}{25} + 3\frac{3}{5} = 5\frac{16}{25}$

18) $3\frac{1}{15} + 2\frac{2}{10} = 5\frac{4}{15}$

19) $5\frac{6}{7} + 2\frac{1}{3} = 8\frac{4}{21}$

20) $2\frac{1}{8} + 3\frac{3}{4} = 5\frac{7}{8}$

21) $2\frac{5}{7} + 2\frac{2}{21} = 4\frac{17}{21}$

22) $4\frac{1}{6} + 1\frac{4}{5} = 5\frac{29}{30}$

23) $3\frac{5}{6} + 1\frac{2}{7} = 5\frac{5}{42}$

24) $2\frac{7}{8} + 3\frac{1}{3} = 6\frac{5}{24}$

25) $3\frac{1}{17} + 1\frac{1}{2} = 4\frac{19}{34}$

26) $1\frac{1}{18} + 1\frac{4}{9} = 2\frac{1}{2}$

Subtracting Mixed Numbers

✎ *Solve and write the answer in lowest terms.*

1) $3\frac{2}{5} - 1\frac{2}{9} =$

2) $5\frac{3}{5} - 1\frac{1}{7} =$

3) $4\frac{2}{5} - 2\frac{2}{7} =$

4) $8\frac{3}{4} - 2\frac{1}{8} =$

5) $9\frac{5}{7} - 7\frac{4}{21} =$

6) $11\frac{7}{12} - 9\frac{5}{6} =$

7) $9\frac{5}{9} - 8\frac{1}{8} =$

8) $13\frac{7}{9} - 11\frac{3}{7} =$

9) $8\frac{7}{12} - 7\frac{3}{8} =$

10) $11\frac{5}{9} - 9\frac{1}{4} =$

11) $6\frac{5}{6} - 2\frac{2}{9} =$

12) $5\frac{7}{8} - 4\frac{1}{3} =$

13) $9\frac{5}{8} - 8\frac{1}{2} =$

14) $4\frac{9}{16} - 2\frac{1}{4} =$

15) $3\frac{2}{3} - 1\frac{2}{15} =$

16) $5\frac{1}{2} - 4\frac{2}{17} =$

17) $5\frac{6}{7} - 2\frac{1}{3} =$

18) $3\frac{3}{7} - 2\frac{2}{21} =$

19) $7\frac{3}{10} - 5\frac{2}{15} =$

20) $4\frac{5}{6} - 2\frac{2}{9} =$

21) $6\frac{3}{7} - 2\frac{2}{9} =$

22) $7\frac{4}{5} - 6\frac{3}{7} =$

23) $10\frac{2}{3} - 9\frac{5}{8} =$

24) $9\frac{3}{4} - 7\frac{4}{9} =$

25) $15\frac{4}{5} - 13\frac{12}{25} =$

26) $13\frac{5}{12} - 7\frac{5}{24} =$

Subtracting Mixed Numbers - Answers

✎ *Solve and write the answer in lowest terms.*

1) $3\frac{2}{5} - 1\frac{2}{9} = 2\frac{8}{45}$

2) $5\frac{3}{5} - 1\frac{1}{7} = 4\frac{16}{35}$

3) $4\frac{2}{5} - 2\frac{2}{7} = 2\frac{4}{35}$

4) $8\frac{3}{4} - 2\frac{1}{8} = 6\frac{5}{8}$

5) $9\frac{5}{7} - 7\frac{4}{21} = 2\frac{11}{21}$

6) $11\frac{7}{12} - 9\frac{5}{6} = 1\frac{3}{4}$

7) $9\frac{5}{9} - 8\frac{1}{8} = 1\frac{31}{72}$

8) $13\frac{7}{9} - 11\frac{3}{7} = 2\frac{22}{63}$

9) $8\frac{7}{12} - 7\frac{3}{8} = 1\frac{5}{24}$

10) $11\frac{5}{9} - 9\frac{1}{4} = 2\frac{11}{36}$

11) $6\frac{5}{6} - 2\frac{2}{9} = 4\frac{11}{18}$

12) $5\frac{7}{8} - 4\frac{1}{3} = 1\frac{13}{24}$

13) $9\frac{5}{8} - 8\frac{1}{2} = 1\frac{1}{8}$

14) $4\frac{9}{16} - 2\frac{1}{4} = 2\frac{5}{16}$

15) $3\frac{2}{3} - 1\frac{2}{15} = 2\frac{8}{15}$

16) $5\frac{1}{2} - 4\frac{2}{17} = 1\frac{13}{34}$

17) $5\frac{6}{7} - 2\frac{1}{3} = 3\frac{11}{21}$

18) $3\frac{3}{7} - 2\frac{2}{21} = 1\frac{1}{3}$

19) $7\frac{3}{10} - 5\frac{2}{15} = 2\frac{1}{6}$

20) $4\frac{5}{6} - 2\frac{2}{9} = 2\frac{11}{18}$

21) $6\frac{3}{7} - 2\frac{2}{9} = 4\frac{13}{63}$

22) $7\frac{4}{5} - 6\frac{3}{7} = 1\frac{13}{35}$

23) $10\frac{2}{3} - 9\frac{5}{8} = 1\frac{1}{24}$

24) $9\frac{3}{4} - 7\frac{4}{9} = 2\frac{11}{36}$

25) $15\frac{4}{5} - 13\frac{12}{25} = 2\frac{8}{25}$

26) $13\frac{5}{12} - 7\frac{5}{24} = 6\frac{5}{24}$

Name: ....   Date: ....

Multiplying Mixed Numbers

✎ *Solve and write the answer in lowest terms.*

1) $1\frac{1}{8} \times 1\frac{3}{4} =$

2) $3\frac{1}{5} \times 2\frac{2}{7} =$

3) $2\frac{1}{8} \times 1\frac{2}{9} =$

4) $2\frac{3}{8} \times 2\frac{2}{5} =$

5) $1\frac{1}{2} \times 5\frac{2}{3} =$

6) $3\frac{1}{2} \times 6\frac{2}{3} =$

7) $9\frac{1}{2} \times 2\frac{1}{6} =$

8) $2\frac{5}{8} \times 8\frac{3}{5} =$

9) $3\frac{4}{5} \times 4\frac{2}{3} =$

10) $5\frac{1}{3} \times 2\frac{2}{7} =$

11) $6\frac{1}{3} \times 3\frac{3}{4} =$

12) $7\frac{2}{3} \times 1\frac{8}{9} =$

13) $8\frac{1}{2} \times 2\frac{1}{6} =$

14) $4\frac{1}{5} \times 8\frac{2}{3} =$

15) $3\frac{1}{8} \times 5\frac{2}{3} =$

16) $2\frac{2}{7} \times 6\frac{2}{5} =$

17) $2\frac{3}{8} \times 7\frac{2}{3} =$

18) $1\frac{7}{8} \times 8\frac{2}{3} =$

19) $9\frac{1}{2} \times 3\frac{1}{5} =$

20) $2\frac{5}{8} \times 4\frac{1}{3} =$

21) $6\frac{1}{3} \times 3\frac{2}{5} =$

22) $5\frac{3}{4} \times 2\frac{2}{7} =$

23) $9\frac{1}{4} \times 2\frac{1}{3} =$

24) $3\frac{3}{7} \times 7\frac{2}{5} =$

25) $4\frac{1}{4} \times 3\frac{2}{5} =$

26) $7\frac{2}{3} \times 3\frac{2}{5} =$

Multiplying Mixed Numbers - Answers

✎ *Solve and write the answer in lowest terms.*

1) $1\frac{1}{8} \times 1\frac{3}{4} = 1\frac{31}{32}$

2) $3\frac{1}{5} \times 2\frac{2}{7} = 7\frac{11}{35}$

3) $2\frac{1}{8} \times 1\frac{2}{9} = 2\frac{43}{72}$

4) $2\frac{3}{8} \times 2\frac{2}{5} = 5\frac{7}{10}$

5) $1\frac{1}{2} \times 5\frac{2}{3} = 8\frac{1}{2}$

6) $3\frac{1}{2} \times 6\frac{2}{3} = 23\frac{1}{3}$

7) $9\frac{1}{2} \times 2\frac{1}{6} = 20\frac{7}{12}$

8) $2\frac{5}{8} \times 8\frac{3}{5} = 22\frac{23}{40}$

9) $3\frac{4}{5} \times 4\frac{2}{3} = 17\frac{11}{15}$

10) $5\frac{1}{3} \times 2\frac{2}{7} = 12\frac{4}{21}$

11) $6\frac{1}{3} \times 3\frac{3}{4} = 23\frac{3}{4}$

12) $7\frac{2}{3} \times 1\frac{8}{9} = 14\frac{13}{27}$

13) $8\frac{1}{2} \times 2\frac{1}{6} = 18\frac{5}{12}$

14) $4\frac{1}{5} \times 8\frac{2}{3} = 36\frac{2}{5}$

15) $3\frac{1}{8} \times 5\frac{2}{3} = 17\frac{17}{24}$

16) $2\frac{2}{7} \times 6\frac{2}{5} = 14\frac{22}{35}$

17) $2\frac{3}{8} \times 7\frac{2}{3} = 18\frac{5}{24}$

18) $1\frac{7}{8} \times 8\frac{2}{3} = 16\frac{1}{4}$

19) $9\frac{1}{2} \times 3\frac{1}{5} = 30\frac{2}{5}$

20) $2\frac{5}{8} \times 4\frac{1}{3} = 11\frac{3}{8}$

21) $6\frac{1}{3} \times 3\frac{2}{5} = 21\frac{8}{15}$

22) $5\frac{3}{4} \times 2\frac{2}{7} = 13\frac{1}{7}$

23) $9\frac{1}{4} \times 2\frac{1}{3} = 21\frac{7}{12}$

24) $3\frac{3}{7} \times 7\frac{2}{5} = 25\frac{13}{35}$

25) $4\frac{1}{4} \times 3\frac{2}{5} = 14\frac{9}{20}$

26) $7\frac{2}{3} \times 3\frac{2}{5} = 26\frac{1}{15}$

Dividing Mixed Numbers

✎ *Solve and write the answer in lowest terms.*

1) $9\frac{1}{2} \div 2\frac{3}{5} =$

14) $2\frac{5}{8} \div 1\frac{8}{9} =$

2) $2\frac{3}{8} \div 1\frac{2}{5} =$

15) $5\frac{6}{7} \div 2\frac{3}{4} =$

3) $5\frac{3}{4} \div 2\frac{2}{7} =$

16) $1\frac{3}{5} \div 2\frac{3}{8} =$

4) $8\frac{1}{3} \div 4\frac{1}{4} =$

17) $5\frac{3}{4} \div 3\frac{2}{5} =$

5) $7\frac{2}{5} \div 3\frac{3}{4} =$

18) $2\frac{3}{4} \div 3\frac{1}{5} =$

6) $2\frac{4}{5} \div 3\frac{2}{3} =$

19) $3\frac{2}{3} \div 1\frac{2}{5} =$

7) $8\frac{3}{5} \div 4\frac{3}{4} =$

20) $4\frac{1}{4} \div 2\frac{2}{3} =$

8) $6\frac{3}{4} \div 2\frac{2}{9} =$

21) $3\frac{5}{6} \div 2\frac{4}{5} =$

9) $5\frac{2}{7} \div 2\frac{2}{9} =$

22) $2\frac{1}{8} \div 1\frac{3}{4} =$

10) $2\frac{2}{5} \div 3\frac{3}{5} =$

23) $5\frac{1}{2} \div 2\frac{2}{5} =$

11) $4\frac{3}{7} \div 1\frac{7}{8} =$

24) $3\frac{4}{7} \div 2\frac{2}{3} =$

12) $2\frac{5}{7} \div 2\frac{4}{5} =$

25) $2\frac{4}{5} \div 3\frac{5}{6} =$

13) $8\frac{3}{5} \div 6\frac{1}{5} =$

26) $2\frac{3}{7} \div 3\frac{2}{3} =$

Dividing Mixed Numbers - Answers

✎ *Solve and write the answer in lowest terms.*

1) $9\frac{1}{2} \div 2\frac{3}{5} = 3\frac{17}{26}$

2) $2\frac{3}{8} \div 1\frac{2}{5} = 1\frac{39}{56}$

3) $5\frac{3}{4} \div 2\frac{2}{7} = 2\frac{33}{64}$

4) $8\frac{1}{3} \div 4\frac{1}{4} = 1\frac{49}{51}$

5) $7\frac{2}{5} \div 3\frac{3}{4} = 1\frac{73}{75}$

6) $2\frac{4}{5} \div 3\frac{2}{3} = \frac{42}{55}$

7) $8\frac{3}{5} \div 4\frac{3}{4} = 1\frac{77}{95}$

8) $6\frac{3}{4} \div 2\frac{2}{9} = 3\frac{3}{80}$

9) $5\frac{2}{7} \div 2\frac{2}{9} = 2\frac{53}{140}$

10) $2\frac{2}{5} \div 3\frac{3}{5} = \frac{2}{3}$

11) $4\frac{3}{7} \div 1\frac{7}{8} = 2\frac{88}{105}$

12) $2\frac{5}{7} \div 2\frac{4}{5} = \frac{95}{98}$

13) $8\frac{3}{5} \div 6\frac{1}{5} = 1\frac{12}{31}$

14) $2\frac{5}{8} \div 1\frac{8}{9} = 1\frac{53}{136}$

15) $5\frac{6}{7} \div 2\frac{3}{4} = 2\frac{10}{77}$

16) $1\frac{3}{5} \div 2\frac{3}{8} = \frac{64}{95}$

17) $5\frac{3}{4} \div 3\frac{2}{5} = 1\frac{47}{68}$

18) $2\frac{3}{4} \div 3\frac{1}{5} = \frac{55}{64}$

19) $3\frac{2}{3} \div 1\frac{2}{5} = 2\frac{13}{21}$

20) $4\frac{1}{4} \div 2\frac{2}{3} = 1\frac{19}{32}$

21) $3\frac{5}{6} \div 2\frac{4}{5} = 1\frac{31}{84}$

22) $2\frac{1}{8} \div 1\frac{3}{4} = 1\frac{3}{14}$

23) $5\frac{1}{2} \div 2\frac{2}{5} = 2\frac{7}{24}$

24) $3\frac{4}{7} \div 2\frac{2}{3} = 1\frac{19}{56}$

25) $2\frac{4}{5} \div 3\frac{5}{6} = \frac{84}{115}$

26) $2\frac{3}{7} \div 3\frac{2}{3} = \frac{51}{77}$

Comparing Decimals

✎ **Compare. Use >, =, and <**

1) 0.88 ☐ 0.088

2) 0.56 ☐ 0.57

3) 0.99 ☐ 0.89

4) 1.55 ☐ 1.65

5) 1.58 ☐ 1.75

6) 2.91 ☐ 2.85

7) 14.56 ☐ 1.456

8) 17.85 ☐ 17.89

9) 21.52 ☐ 21.052

10) 11.12 ☐ 11.03

11) 9.650 ☐ 9.65

12) 8.578 ☐ 8.568

13) 3.15 ☐ 0.315

14) 16.61 ☐ 16.16

15) 18.581 ☐ 8.991

16) 25.05 ☐ 2.505

17) 4.55 ☐ 4.65

18) 0.158 ☐ 1.58

19) 0.881 ☐ 0.871

20) 0.505 ☐ 0.510

21) 0.772 ☐ 0.777

22) 0.5 ☐ 0.500

23) 16.89 ☐ 15.89

24) 12.25 ☐ 12.35

25) 5.82 ☐ 5.69

26) 1.320 ☐ 1.032

27) 0.082 ☐ 0.088

28) 0.99 ☐ 0.099

29) 2.560 ☐ 1.950

30) 0.770 ☐ 0.707

31) 15.54 ☐ 1.554

32) 0.323 ☐ 0.332

Comparing Decimals - Answers

✎ *Compare. Use >, =, and <*

1) $0.88 > 0.088$

2) $0.56 < 0.57$

3) $0.99 > 0.89$

4) $1.55 < 1.65$

5) $1.58 < 1.75$

6) $2.91 > 2.85$

7) $14.56 > 1.456$

8) $17.85 < 17.89$

9) $21.52 > 21.052$

10) $11.12 > 11.03$

11) $9.650 = 9.65$

12) $8.578 > 8.568$

13) $3.15 > 0.315$

14) $16.61 > 16.16$

15) $18.581 > 8.991$

16) $25.05 > 2.505$

17) $4.55 < 4.65$

18) $0.158 < 1.58$

19) $0.881 > 0.871$

20) $0.505 < 0.510$

21) $0.772 < 0.777$

22) $0.5 = 0.500$

23) $16.89 > 15.89$

24) $12.25 < 12.35$

25) $5.82 > 5.69$

26) $1.320 > 1.032$

27) $0.082 < 0.088$

28) $0.99 > 0.099$

29) $2.560 > 1.950$

30) $0.770 > 0.707$

31) $15.54 > 1.554$

32) $0.323 < 0.332$

Rounding Decimals

✎ *Round each number to the underlined place value.*

1) 2.814 =

2) 3.562 =

3) 12.125 =

4) 15.5 =

5) 1.981 =

6) 14.215 =

7) 17.548 =

8) 25.508 =

9) 31.089 =

10) 69.345 =

11) 9.457 =

12) 12.901 =

13) 2.658 =

14) 32.565 =

15) 6.058 =

16) 98.108 =

17) 27.705 =

18) 36.75 =

19) 9.08 =

20) 7.185 =

21) 22.547 =

22) 66.098 =

23) 87.75 =

24) 18.541 =

25) 10.258 =

26) 13.456 =

27) 71.084 =

28) 29.23 =

29) 45.55 =

30) 91.08 =

31) 83.433 =

32) 74.64 =

Rounding Decimals - Answers

✎ *Round each number to the underlined place value.*

1) 2.814 = 3

2) 3.562 = 3.56

3) 12.125 = 12.13

4) 15.5 = 16

5) 1.981 = 1.98

6) 14.215 = 14.2

7) 17.548 = 17.55

8) 25.508 = 25.51

9) 31.089 = 31

10) 69.345 = 69.3

11) 9.457 = 9.46

12) 12.901 = 13

13) 2.658 = 2.66

14) 32.565 = 32.6

15) 6.058 = 6.06

16) 98.108 = 98.11

17) 27.705 = 27.7

18) 36.75 = 37

19) 9.08 = 9.1

20) 7.185 = 7.2

21) 22.547 = 22.55

22) 66.098 = 66.1

23) 87.75 = 88

24) 18.541 = 18.5

25) 10.258 = 10.26

26) 13.456 = 13.5

27) 71.084 = 71.08

28) 29.23 = 29

29) 45.55 = 45.6

30) 91.08 = 91

33) 83.433 = 83

34) 74.64 = 74.6

Adding and Subtracting Decimals

✎ **Solve.**

1) 15.63 + 19.64 =

2) 16.38 + 17.59 =

3) 75.31 − 59.69 =

4) 49.38 − 29.89 =

5) 24.32 + 26.45 =

6) 36.25 + 18.37 =

7) 47.85 − 35.12 =

8) 85.65 − 67.48 =

9) 25.49 + 34.18 =

10) 19.99 + 48.66 =

11) 46.32 − 27.77 =

12) 54.62 − 48.12 =

13) 24.42 + 16.54 =

14) 52.13 + 12.32 =

15) 82.36 − 78.65 =

16) 64.12 − 49.15 =

17) 36.41 + 24.52 =

18) 85.96 − 74.63 =

19) 52.62 − 42.54 =

20) 21.20 + 24.58 =

21) 32.15 + 17.17 =

22) 96.32 − 85.54 =

23) 89.78 − 69.85 =

24) 29.28 + 39.79 =

25) 11.11 + 19.99 =

26) 28.82 + 20.88 =

27) 63.14 − 28.91 =

28) 56.61 − 49.72 =

29) 26.13 + 31.13 =

30) 30.19 + 20.87 =

31) 66.24 − 59.10 =

32) 89.31 − 72.17 =

Homework: #.....

Adding and Subtracting Decimals - Answers

✍ *Solve.*

1) $15.63 + 19.64 = 35.27$

2) $16.38 + 17.59 = 33.97$

3) $75.31 - 59.69 = 15.62$

4) $49.38 - 29.89 = 19.49$

5) $24.32 + 26.45 = 50.77$

6) $36.25 + 18.37 = 54.62$

7) $47.85 - 35.12 = 12.73$

8) $85.65 - 67.48 = 18.17$

9) $25.49 + 34.18 = 59.67$

10) $19.99 + 48.66 = 68.65$

11) $46.32 - 27.77 = 18.55$

12) $54.62 - 48.12 = 6.5$

13) $24.42 + 16.54 = 40.96$

14) $52.13 + 12.32 = 64.45$

15) $82.36 - 78.65 = 3.71$

16) $64.12 - 49.15 = 14.97$

17) $36.41 + 24.52 = 60.93$

18) $85.96 - 74.63 = 11.33$

19) $52.62 - 42.54 = 10.08$

20) $21.20 + 24.58 = 45.78$

21) $32.15 + 17.17 = 49.32$

22) $96.32 - 85.54 = 10.78$

23) $89.78 - 69.85 = 19.93$

24) $29.28 + 39.79 = 69.07$

25) $11.11 + 19.99 = 31.1$

26) $28.82 + 20.88 = 49.7$

27) $63.14 - 28.91 = 34.23$

28) $56.61 - 49.72 = 6.89$

29) $26.13 + 31.13 = 57.26$

30) $30.19 + 20.87 = 51.06$

31) $66.24 - 59.10 = 7.14$

32) $89.31 - 72.17 = 17.14$

Homework: #.....

Multiplying and Dividing Decimals

✍ *Solve.*

1) $11.2 \times 0.4 =$

2) $13.5 \times 0.8 =$

3) $42.2 \div 2 =$

4) $54.6 \div 6 =$

5) $23.1 \times 0.3 =$

6) $1.2 \times 0.7 =$

7) $5.5 \div 0.5 =$

8) $64.8 \div 8 =$

9) $1.4 \times 0.5 =$

10) $4.5 \times 0.3 =$

11) $88.8 \div 4 =$

12) $10.5 \div 5 =$

13) $2.2 \times 0.3 =$

14) $0.2 \times 0.52 =$

15) $95.7 \div 100 =$

16) $36.6 \div 6 =$

17) $3.2 \times 2 =$

18) $4.1 \times 0.5 =$

19) $68.4 \div 2 =$

20) $27.9 \div 9 =$

21) $3.5 \times 4 =$

22) $4.8 \times 0.5 =$

23) $6.4 \div 4 =$

24) $72.8 \div 0.8 =$

25) $1.8 \times 3 =$

26) $6.5 \times 0.2 =$

27) $93.6 \div 3 =$

28) $45.15 \div 0.5 =$

29) $13.2 \times 0.4 =$

30) $11.2 \times 5 =$

31) $7.2 \div 0.8 =$

32) $96.4 \div 0.2 =$

Homework: #.....

Multiplying and Dividing Decimals - Answers

✎ *Solve.*

1) $11.2 \times 0.4 = 4.48$

2) $13.5 \times 0.8 = 10.8$

3) $42.2 \div 2 = 21.1$

4) $54.6 \div 6 = 9.1$

5) $23.1 \times 0.3 = 6.93$

6) $1.2 \times 0.7 = 0.84$

7) $5.5 \div 5 = 1.1$

8) $64.8 \div 8 = 8.1$

9) $1.4 \times 0.5 = 0.7$

10) $4.5 \times 0.3 = 1.35$

11) $88.8 \div 4 = 22.2$

12) $10.5 \div 5 = 2.1$

13) $2.2 \times 0.3 = 0.66$

14) $0.2 \times 0.52 = 0.104$

15) $95.7 \div 100 = 0.957$

16) $36.6 \div 6 = 6.1$

17) $3.2 \times 2 = 6.4$

18) $4.1 \times 0.5 = 2.05$

19) $68.4 \div 2 = 34.2$

20) $27.9 \div 9 = 3.1$

21) $3.5 \times 4 = 14$

22) $4.8 \times 0.5 = 2.4$

23) $6.4 \div 4 = 1.6$

24) $72.8 \div 0.8 = 91$

25) $1.8 \times 3 = 5.4$

26) $6.5 \times 0.2 = 1.3$

27) $93.6 \div 3 = 31.2$

28) $45.15 \div 0.5 = 90.3$

29) $13.2 \times 0.4 = 5.28$

30) $11.2 \times 5 = 56$

31) $7.2 \div 0.8 = 9$

32) $96.4 \div 0.2 = 482$

Adding and Subtracting Integers

✍ **Solve.**

1) $-(8) + 13 =$

2) $17 - (-12 - 8) =$

3) $(-15) + (-4) =$

4) $(-14) + (-8) + 9 =$

5) $-(23) + 19 =$

6) $(-7 + 5) - 9 =$

7) $28 + (-32) =$

8) $(-11) + (-9) + 5 =$

9) $25 - (8 - 7) =$

10) $-(29) + 17 =$

11) $(-38) + (-3) + 29 =$

12) $15 - (-7 + 9) =$

13) $24 - (8 - 2) =$

14) $(-7 + 4) - 9 =$

15) $(-17) + (-3) + 9 =$

16) $(-26) + (-7) + 8 =$

17) $(-9) + (-11) =$

18) $8 - (-23 - 13) =$

19) $(-16) + (-2) =$

20) $25 - (7 - 4) =$

21) $23 + (-12) =$

22) $(-18) + (-6) =$

23) $17 - (-21 - 7) =$

24) $-(28) - (-16) + 5 =$

25) $(-9 + 4) - 8 =$

26) $(-28) + (-6) + 17 =$

27) $-(21) - (-15) + 9 =$

28) $(-31) + (-6) =$

29) $(-17) + (-11) + 14 =$

30) $(-29) + (-10) + 13 =$

31) $-(24) - (-12) + 5 =$

32) $8 - (-19 - 10) =$

Adding and Subtracting Integers - Answers

✎ *Solve.*

1) $-(8) + 13 = 5$

2) $17 - (-12 - 8) = 37$

3) $(-15) + (-4) = -19$

4) $(-14) + (-8) + 9 = -13$

5) $-(23) + 19 = -4$

6) $(-7 + 5) - 9 = -11$

7) $28 + (-32) = -4$

8) $(-11) + (-9) + 5 = -15$

9) $25 - (8 - 7) = 24$

10) $-(29) + 17 = -12$

11) $(-38) + (-3) + 29 = -12$

12) $15 - (-7 + 9) = 13$

13) $24 - (8 - 2) = 18$

14) $(-7 + 4) - 9 = -12$

15) $(-17) + (-3) + 9 = -11$

16) $(-26) + (-7) + 8 = -25$

17) $(-9) + (-11) = -20$

18) $8 - (-23 - 13) = 44$

19) $(-16) + (-2) = -18$

20) $25 - (7 - 4) = 22$

21) $23 + (-12) = 11$

22) $(-18) + (-6) = -24$

23) $17 - (-21 - 7) = 45$

24) $-(28) - (-16) + 5 = -7$

25) $(-9 + 4) - 8 = -13$

26) $(-28) + (-6) + 17 = -17$

27) $-(21) - (-15) + 9 = 3$

28) $(-31) + (-6) = -37$

29) $(-17) + (-11) + 14 = -14$

30) $(-29) + (-10) + 13 = -26$

31) $-(24) - (-12) + 5 = -7$

32) $8 - (-19 - 10) = 37$

Multiplying and Dividing Integers

✎ *Solve.*

1) $(-9) \times (-8) =$

2) $6 \times (-6) =$

3) $49 \div (-7) =$

4) $(-64) \div 8 =$

5) $(4) \times (-6) =$

6) $(-9) \times (-11) =$

7) $(10) \div (-5) =$

8) $144 \div (-12) =$

9) $(10) \times (-2) =$

10) $(-8) \times (-2) \times 5 =$

11) $(8) \div (-2) =$

12) $45 \div (-15) =$

13) $(5) \times (-7) =$

14) $(-6) \times (-5) \times 4 =$

15) $(12) \div (-6) =$

16) $(14) \div (-7) =$

17) $196 \div (-14) =$

18) $(27 - 13) \times (-2) =$

19) $125 \div (-5) =$

20) $66 \div (-6) =$

21) $(-6) \times (-5) \times 3 =$

22) $(15 - 6) \times (-3) =$

23) $(32 - 24) \div (-4) =$

24) $72 \div (-6) =$

25) $(-14 + 8) \times (-7) =$

26) $(-3) \times (-9) \times 3 =$

27) $84 \div (-12) =$

28) $(-12) \times (-10) =$

29) $25 \times (-4) =$

30) $(-3) \times (-5) \times 5 =$

31) $(15) \div (-3) =$

32) $(-18) \div (3) =$

Multiplying and Dividing Integers - Answers

✎ *Solve.*

1) $(-9) \times (-8) = 72$

2) $6 \times (-6) = -36$

3) $49 \div (-7) = -7$

4) $(-64) \div 8 = -8$

5) $(4) \times (-6) = -24$

6) $(-9) \times (-11) = 99$

7) $(10) \div (-5) = -2$

8) $144 \div (-12) = -12$

9) $(10) \times (-2) = -20$

10) $(-8) \times (-2) \times 5 = 80$

11) $(8) \div (-2) = -4$

12) $45 \div (-15) = -3$

13) $(5) \times (-7) = -35$

14) $(-6) \times (-5) \times 5 = 150$

15) $(12) \div (-6) = -2$

16) $(14) \div (-7) = -2$

17) $196 \div (-14) = -14$

18) $(27 - 13) \times (-2) = -28$

19) $125 \div (-5) = 25$

20) $66 \div (-6) = -11$

21) $(-6) \times (-5) \times 3 = 90$

22) $(15 - 6) \times (-3) = -27$

23) $(32 - 24) \div (-4) = -2$

24) $72 \div (-6) = -12$

25) $(-14 + 8) \times (-7) = 42$

26) $(-3) \times (-9) \times 3 = 81$

27) $84 \div (-12) = -7$

28) $(-12) \times (-10) = 120$

29) $25 \times (-4) = -100$

30) $(-3) \times (-5) \times 5 = 75$

31) $(15) \div (-3) = -5$

32) $(-18) \div (3) = -6$

Order of Operation

✎ *Calculate.*

1) $18 + (32 \div 4) =$

2) $(3 \times 8) \div (-2) =$

3) $67 - (4 \times 8) =$

4) $(-11) \times (8 - 3) =$

5) $(18 - 7) \times (6) =$

6) $(6 \times 10) \div (12 + 3) =$

7) $(13 \times 2) - (24 \div 6) =$

8) $(-5) + (4 \times 3) + 8 =$

9) $(4 \times 2^3) + (16 - 9) =$

10) $(3^2 \times 7) \div (-2 + 1) =$

11) $[-2(48 \div 2^3)] - 6 =$

12) $(-4) + (7 \times 8) + 18 =$

13) $(3 \times 7) + (16 - 7) =$

14) $[3^3 \times (48 \div 2^3)] \div (-2) =$

15) $(14 \times 3) - (3^4 \div 9) =$

16) $(96 \div 12) \times (-3) =$

17) $(48 \div 2^2) \times (-2) =$

18) $(56 \div 7) \times (-5) =$

19) $(-2^2) + (7 \times 9) - 21 =$

20) $(2^4 - 9) \times (-6) =$

21) $[4^3 \times (50 \div 5^2)] \div (-16) =$

22) $(3^2 \times 4^2) \div (-4 + 2) =$

23) $6^2 - (-6 \times 4) + 3 =$

24) $4^2 - (5^2 \times 3) =$

25) $(-4) + (12^2 \div 3^2) - 7^2 =$

26) $(3^2 \times 5) + (-5^2 - 9) =$

27) $2[(3^2 \times 5) \times (-6)] =$

28) $(11^2 - 2^2) - (-7^2) =$

29) $(2^3 \times 3) - (49 \div 7) =$

30) $3[(3^2 \times 5) + (25 \div 5)] =$

31) $(6^2 \times 5) \div (-5) =$

32) $2^2[(6^3 \div 12) - (3^4 \div 27)] =$

Order of Operation - Answers

✎ *Calculate.*

1) $18 + (32 \div 4) = 26$

2) $(3 \times 8) \div (-2) = -12$

3) $67 - (4 \times 8) = 35$

4) $(-11) \times (8 - 3) = -55$

5) $(18 - 7) \times (6) = 66$

6) $(6 \times 10) \div (12 + 3) = 4$

7) $(13 \times 2) - (24 \div 6) = 22$

8) $(-5) + (4 \times 3) + 8 = 15$

9) $(4 \times 2^3) + (16 - 9) = 39$

10) $(3^2 \times 7) \div (-2 + 1) = -63$

11) $[-2(48 \div 2^3)] - 6 = -18$

12) $(-4) + (7 \times 8) + 18 = 70$

13) $(3 \times 7) + (16 - 7) = 30$

14) $[3^3 \times (48 \div 2^3)] \div (-2) = -81$

15) $(14 \times 3) - (3^4 \div 9) = 33$

16) $(96 \div 12) \times (-3) = -24$

17) $(48 \div 2^2) \times (-2) = -24$

18) $(56 \div 7) \times (-5) = -40$

19) $(-2^2) + (7 \times 9) - 21 = 38$

20) $(2^4 - 9) \times (-6) = -42$

21) $[4^3 \times (50 \div 5^2)] \div (-16) = -8$

22) $(3^2 \times 4^2) \div (-4 + 2) = -72$

23) $6^2 - (-6 \times 4) + 3 = 63$

24) $4^2 - (5^2 \times 3) = -59$

25) $(-4) + (12^2 \div 3^2) - 7^2 = -37$

26) $(3^2 \times 5) + (-5^2 - 9) = 11$

27) $2[(3^2 \times 5) \times (-6)] = -540$

28) $(11^2 - 2^2) - (-7^2) = 166$

29) $(2^3 \times 3) - (49 \div 7) = 17$

30) $3[(3^2 \times 5) + (25 \div 5)] = 150$

31) $(6^2 \times 5) \div (-5) = -36$

32) $2^2[(6^3 \div 12) - (3^4 \div 27)] = 60$

Integers and Absolute Value

✎ *Calculate.*

1) $5 - |8 - 12| =$

2) $|15| - \dfrac{|-1|}{4} =$

3) $\dfrac{|9 \times -6|}{18} \times \dfrac{|-24|}{8} =$

4) $|13 \times 3| + \dfrac{|-72|}{9} =$

5) $4 - |11 - 18| - |3| =$

6) $|18| - \dfrac{|-1|}{4} =$

7) $\dfrac{|5 \times -8|}{10} \times \dfrac{|-22|}{11} =$

8) $|9 \times 3| + \dfrac{|-36|}{4} =$

9) $|-42 + 7| \times \dfrac{|-2 \times 5|}{10} =$

10) $6 - |17 - 11| - |5| =$

11) $|13| - \dfrac{|-54|}{6} =$

12) $\dfrac{|9 \times -4|}{12} \times \dfrac{|-45|}{9} =$

13) $|-75 + 50| \times \dfrac{|-4 \times 5|}{5} =$

14) $\dfrac{|-26|}{13} \times \dfrac{|-3|}{8} =$

15) $14 - |8 - 18| - |-12| =$

16) $|29| - \dfrac{|-20|}{5} =$

17) $\dfrac{|3 \times 8|}{2} \times \dfrac{|-33|}{3} =$

18) $|-45 + 15| \times \dfrac{|-12 \times 5|}{6} =$

19) $\dfrac{|-50|}{5} \times \dfrac{|-77|}{11} =$

20) $12 - |2 - 7| - |15| =$

21) $|18| - \dfrac{|-45|}{15} =$

22) $\dfrac{|7 \times 8|}{4} \times \dfrac{|-48|}{12} =$

23) $\dfrac{|30 \times 2|}{3} \times |-12| =$

24) $\dfrac{|-36|}{9} \times \dfrac{|-80|}{8} =$

25) $|-35 + 8| \times \dfrac{|-9 \times 5|}{15} =$

26) $|19| - \dfrac{|-18|}{2} =$

27) $14 - |11 - 23| + |2| =$

28) $|-39 + 7| \times \dfrac{|-4 \times 6|}{3} =$

Integers and Absolute Value - Answers

✎ *Calculate.*

1) $5 - |8 - 12| = 1$

2) $|15| - \frac{|-16|}{4} = 11$

3) $\frac{|9 \times -6|}{18} \times \frac{|-24|}{8} = 9$

4) $|13 \times 3| + \frac{|-72|}{9} = 47$

5) $4 - |11 - 18| - |3| = -6$

6) $|18| - \frac{|-12|}{4} = 15$

7) $\frac{|5 \times -8|}{10} \times \frac{|-22|}{11} = 8$

8) $|9 \times 3| + \frac{|-3|}{4} = 36$

9) $|-42 + 7| \times \frac{|-2 \times 5|}{10} = 35$

10) $6 - |17 - 11| - |5| = -5$

11) $|13| - \frac{|-54|}{6} = 4$

12) $\frac{|9 \times -4|}{12} \times \frac{|-45|}{9} = 15$

13) $|-75 + 50| \times \frac{|-4 \times 5|}{5} = 100$

14) $\frac{|-2|}{13} \times \frac{|-32|}{8} = 8$

15) $14 - |8 - 18| - |-12| = -8$

16) $|29| - \frac{|-20|}{5} = 25$

17) $\frac{|3 \times 8|}{2} \times \frac{|-33|}{3} = 132$

18) $|-45 + 15| \times \frac{|-12 \times 5|}{6} = 300$

19) $\frac{|-50|}{5} \times \frac{|-77|}{11} = 70$

20) $12 - |2 - 7| - |15| = -8$

21) $|18| - \frac{|-45|}{15} = 15$

22) $\frac{|7 \times 8|}{4} \times \frac{|-48|}{12} = 56$

23) $\frac{|30 \times 2|}{3} \times |-12| = 240$

24) $\frac{|-36|}{9} \times \frac{|-80|}{8} = 40$

25) $|-35 + 8| \times \frac{|-9 \times 5|}{15} = 81$

26) $|19| - \frac{|-1|}{2} = 10$

27) $14 - |11 - 23| + |2| = 4$

28) $|-39 + 7| \times \frac{|-4 \times 6|}{3} = 256$

Simplifying Ratios

✎ *Simplify each ratio.*

1) $3 : 27 =$ ___ : ___

2) $2 : 8 =$ ___ : ___

3) $\frac{4}{28} = -$

4) $\frac{16}{40} = -$

5) $10 : 30 =$ ___ : ___

6) $5 : 30 =$ ___ : ___

7) $\frac{34}{38} = -$

8) $\frac{45}{63} = -$

9) $10 : 45 =$ ___ : ___

10) $20 : 30 =$ ___ : ___

11) $\frac{40}{64} = -$

12) $\frac{10}{110} = -$

13) $8 : 12 =$ ___ : ___

14) $16 : 20 =$ ___ : ___

15) $\frac{24}{48} = -$

16) $\frac{21}{77} = -$

17) $8 : 24 =$ ___ : ___

18) 9 to $36 =$ ___ : ___

19) $\frac{64}{72} = -$

20) $\frac{45}{60} = -$

21) $12 : 15 =$ ___ : ___

22) $18 : 54 =$ ___ : ___

23) $\frac{36}{54} = -$

24) $\frac{48}{104} = -$

25) $15 : 75 =$ ___ : ___

26) $16 : 48 =$ ___ : ___

27) $\frac{15}{65} = -$

28) $\frac{44}{52} = -$

Simplifying Ratios - Answers

✎ *Simplify each ratio.*

1) $3:27 = 1:9$

2) $2:8 = 1:4$

3) $\frac{4}{28} = \frac{1}{7}$

4) $\frac{16}{40} = \frac{2}{5}$

5) $10:30 = 1:3$

6) $5:30 = 1:6$

7) $\frac{34}{38} = \frac{17}{19}$

8) $\frac{45}{63} = \frac{5}{7}$

9) $10:45 = 2:9$

10) $20:30 = 2:3$

11) $\frac{40}{64} = \frac{5}{8}$

12) $\frac{10}{110} = \frac{1}{11}$

13) $8:12 = 2:3$

14) $16:20 = 4:5$

15) $\frac{24}{48} = \frac{1}{2}$

16) $\frac{21}{77} = \frac{3}{11}$

17) $8:24 = 1:6$

18) $9 \text{ to } 36 = 1 \text{ to } 4$

19) $\frac{64}{72} = \frac{8}{9}$

20) $\frac{45}{60} = \frac{3}{4}$

21) $12:15 = 4:5$

22) $18:54 = 1:3$

23) $\frac{36}{54} = \frac{2}{3}$

24) $\frac{48}{104} = \frac{6}{13}$

25) $15:75 = 1:5$

26) $16:48 = 1:3$

27) $\frac{15}{65} = \frac{3}{13}$

28) $\frac{44}{52} = \frac{11}{13}$

Proportional Ratios

✎ *Solve each proportion for* x.

1) $\frac{4}{7} = \frac{16}{x}$, $x =$ ____

2) $\frac{4}{9} = \frac{x}{18}$, $x =$ ____

3) $\frac{3}{5} = \frac{24}{x}$, $x =$ ____

4) $\frac{3}{10} = \frac{x}{50}$, $x =$ ____

5) $\frac{3}{11} = \frac{15}{x}$, $x =$ ____

6) $\frac{6}{15} = \frac{x}{45}$, $x =$ ____

7) $\frac{6}{19} = \frac{12}{x}$, $x =$ ____

8) $\frac{7}{16} = \frac{x}{32}$, $x =$ ____

9) $\frac{18}{21} = \frac{54}{x}$, $x =$ ____

10) $\frac{13}{15} = \frac{39}{x}$, $x =$ ____

11) $\frac{9}{13} = \frac{72}{x}$, $x =$ ____

12) $\frac{8}{30} = \frac{x}{180}$, $x =$ ____

13) $\frac{3}{19} = \frac{9}{x}$, $x =$ ____

14) $\frac{1}{3} = \frac{x}{90}$, $x =$ ____

15) $\frac{25}{45} = \frac{x}{9}$, $x =$ ____

16) $\frac{1}{6} = \frac{9}{x}$, $x =$ ____

17) $\frac{7}{9} = \frac{63}{x}$, $x =$ ____

18) $\frac{54}{72} = \frac{x}{8}$, $x =$ ____

19) $\frac{32}{40} = \frac{4}{x}$, $x =$ ____

20) $\frac{21}{42} = \frac{x}{6}$, $x =$ ____

21) $\frac{56}{72} = \frac{7}{x}$, $x =$ ____

22) $\frac{1}{14} = \frac{x}{42}$, $x =$ ____

23) $\frac{5}{7} = \frac{75}{x}$, $x =$ ____

24) $\frac{30}{48} = \frac{x}{8}$, $x =$ ____

25) $\frac{36}{88} = \frac{9}{x}$, $x =$ ____

26) $\frac{62}{68} = \frac{x}{34}$, $x =$ ____

27) $\frac{42}{60} = \frac{x}{10}$, $x =$ ____

28) $\frac{8}{9} = \frac{x}{108}$, $x =$ ____

29) $\frac{46}{69} = \frac{x}{3}$, $x =$ ____

30) $\frac{99}{121} = \frac{x}{11}$, $x =$ ____

31) $\frac{19}{21} = \frac{x}{63}$, $x =$ ____

32) $\frac{11}{12} = \frac{x}{48}$, $x =$ ____

Homework: #.....

Proportional Ratios - Answers

✎ *Solve each proportion for x.*

1) $\frac{4}{7} = \frac{16}{x}$, $x = 28$

2) $\frac{4}{9} = \frac{x}{18}$, $x = 8$

3) $\frac{3}{5} = \frac{24}{x}$, $x = 40$

4) $\frac{3}{10} = \frac{x}{50}$, $x = 15$

5) $\frac{3}{11} = \frac{15}{x}$, $x = 55$

6) $\frac{6}{15} = \frac{x}{45}$, $x = 18$

7) $\frac{6}{19} = \frac{12}{x}$, $x = 38$

8) $\frac{7}{16} = \frac{x}{32}$, $x = 14$

9) $\frac{18}{21} = \frac{54}{x}$, $x = 63$

10) $\frac{13}{15} = \frac{39}{x}$, $x = 45$

11) $\frac{9}{13} = \frac{72}{x}$, $x = 104$

12) $\frac{8}{30} = \frac{x}{180}$, $x = 48$

13) $\frac{3}{19} = \frac{9}{x}$, $x = 57$

14) $\frac{1}{3} = \frac{x}{90}$, $x = 30$

15) $\frac{25}{45} = \frac{x}{9}$, $x = 5$

16) $\frac{1}{6} = \frac{9}{x}$, $x = 54$

17) $\frac{7}{9} = \frac{63}{x}$, $x = 81$

18) $\frac{54}{72} = \frac{x}{8}$, $x = 6$

19) $\frac{32}{40} = \frac{4}{x}$, $x = 5$

20) $\frac{21}{42} = \frac{x}{6}$, $x = 3$

21) $\frac{56}{72} = \frac{7}{x}$, $x = 9$

22) $\frac{1}{14} = \frac{x}{42}$, $x = 3$

23) $\frac{5}{7} = \frac{75}{x}$, $x = 105$

24) $\frac{30}{48} = \frac{x}{8}$, $x = 5$

25) $\frac{36}{88} = \frac{9}{x}$, $x = 22$

26) $\frac{62}{68} = \frac{x}{34}$, $x = 31$

27) $\frac{42}{60} = \frac{x}{10}$, $x = 7$

28) $\frac{8}{9} = \frac{x}{108}$, $x = 96$

29) $\frac{46}{69} = \frac{x}{3}$, $x = 2$

30) $\frac{99}{121} = \frac{x}{11}$, $x = 9$

31) $\frac{19}{21} = \frac{x}{63}$, $x = 57$

32) $\frac{11}{12} = \frac{x}{48}$, $x = 44$

Homework: #.....

Create Proportion

✎ *State if each pair of ratios form a proportion.*

1) $\frac{5}{8}$ and $\frac{25}{50}$

2) $\frac{2}{11}$ and $\frac{4}{22}$

3) $\frac{2}{5}$ and $\frac{8}{20}$

4) $\frac{3}{11}$ and $\frac{9}{33}$

5) $\frac{5}{10}$ and $\frac{15}{30}$

6) $\frac{4}{13}$ and $\frac{8}{24}$

7) $\frac{6}{9}$ and $\frac{24}{36}$

8) $\frac{7}{12}$ and $\frac{14}{20}$

9) $\frac{3}{8}$ and $\frac{27}{72}$

10) $\frac{12}{20}$ and $\frac{36}{60}$

11) $\frac{11}{12}$ and $\frac{55}{60}$

12) $\frac{12}{15}$ and $\frac{24}{25}$

13) $\frac{15}{19}$ and $\frac{20}{38}$

14) $\frac{10}{14}$ and $\frac{40}{56}$

15) $\frac{11}{13}$ and $\frac{44}{39}$

16) $\frac{15}{16}$ and $\frac{30}{32}$

17) $\frac{17}{19}$ and $\frac{34}{48}$

18) $\frac{5}{18}$ and $\frac{15}{54}$

19) $\frac{3}{14}$ and $\frac{18}{42}$

20) $\frac{7}{11}$ and $\frac{14}{32}$

21) $\frac{8}{11}$ and $\frac{32}{44}$

22) $\frac{9}{13}$ and $\frac{18}{26}$

✎ *Solve.*

23) The ratio of boys to girls in a class is 5:6. If there are 25 boys in the class, how many girls are in that class? _____

24) The ratio of red marbles to blue marbles in a bag is 4:7. If there are 77 marbles in the bag, how many of the marbles are red? _____

25) You can buy 8 cans of green beans at a supermarket for $3.20. How much does it cost to buy 48 cans of green beans? _____

Create Proportion - Answers

✍ *State if each pair of ratios form a proportion.*

1) $\frac{5}{8}$ and $\frac{25}{50}$, *No*

2) $\frac{2}{11}$ and $\frac{4}{22}$, *Yes*

3) $\frac{2}{5}$ and $\frac{8}{20}$, *Yes*

4) $\frac{3}{11}$ and $\frac{9}{33}$, *Yes*

5) $\frac{5}{10}$ and $\frac{15}{30}$, *Yes*

6) $\frac{4}{13}$ and $\frac{8}{24}$, *No*

7) $\frac{6}{9}$ and $\frac{24}{36}$, *Yes*

8) $\frac{7}{12}$ and $\frac{14}{20}$, *No*

9) $\frac{3}{8}$ and $\frac{27}{72}$, *Yes*

10) $\frac{12}{20}$ and $\frac{36}{60}$, *Yes*

11) $\frac{11}{12}$ and $\frac{55}{60}$, *Yes*

12) $\frac{12}{15}$ and $\frac{24}{25}$, *No*

13) $\frac{15}{19}$ and $\frac{20}{38}$, *No*

14) $\frac{10}{14}$ and $\frac{40}{56}$, *Yes*

15) $\frac{11}{13}$ and $\frac{44}{39}$, *No*

16) $\frac{15}{16}$ and $\frac{30}{32}$, *Yes*

17) $\frac{17}{19}$ and $\frac{34}{38}$, *Yes*

18) $\frac{5}{18}$ and $\frac{15}{54}$, *Yes*

19) $\frac{3}{14}$ and $\frac{18}{42}$, *No*

20) $\frac{7}{11}$ and $\frac{14}{32}$, *No*

21) $\frac{8}{11}$ and $\frac{32}{44}$, *Yes*

22) $\frac{9}{13}$ and $\frac{18}{26}$, *Yes*

✍ *Solve.*

23) The ratio of boys to girls in a class is 5:6. If there are 25 boys in the class, how many girls are in that class? **30 girls**

24) The ratio of red marbles to blue marbles in a bag is 4:7. If there are 77 marbles in the bag, how many of the marbles are red? **28 red marbles**

25) You can buy 8 cans of green beans at a supermarket for $3.20. How much does it cost to buy 48 cans of green beans? **$19.20**

Name: ....

Date: ....

Homework: #.....

Similarity and Ratios

✎ *Each pair of figures is similar. Find the missing side.*

1)

2)

3)

4)

5)

6)

7)

8)

Similarity and Ratios - Answers

✎ *Each pair of figures is similar. Find the missing side.*

1) *5*

2) *24*

3) *3*

4) *32*

5) *9*

6) *8*

7) *8*

8) *17*

Simple Interest

✎ *Determine the simple interest for following loans.*

1) $440 at 5% for 6 years. $__

2) $460 at 2.5% for 4 years. $_

3) $500 at 3% for 5 years. $__

4) $550 at 9% for 2 years. $__

5) $690 at 5% for 6 months. $__

6) $620 at 7% for 3 years. $__

7) $650 at 4.5% for 10 years. $__

8) $850 at 4% for 2 years. $__

9) $640 at 7% for 3 years. $__

10) $300 at 9% for 9 months. $__

11) $760 at 8% for 2 years. $_

12) $910 at 5% for 5 years. $__

13) $540 at 3% for 6 years. $__

14) $780 at 2.5% for 4 years. $__

15) $1,600 at 7% for 3 months. $__

16) $310 at 4% for 4 years. $__

17) $950 at 6% for 5 years. $__

18) $280 at 8% for 7 years. $__

19) $310 at 6% for 3 years. $__

20) $990 at 5% for 4 months. $___

21) $380 at 6% for 5 years. $__

22) $580 at 6% for 4 years. $__

23) $1,200 at 4% for5 years. $__

24) $3,100 at 5% for 6 years. $__

25) $5,200 at 8% for 2 years. $__

26) $1,400 at 4% for 3 years. $__

27) $300 at 3% for 8 months. $__

28) $150 at 3.5% for 4 years. $__

29) $170 at 6% for 2 years. $__

30) $940 at 8% for 5 years. $__

31) $960 at 1.5% for 8 years. $_

32) $240 at 5% for 4 months. $__

33) $280 at 2% for 5 years. $__

34) $880 at 3% for 2 years. $__

35) $2,200 at 4.5% for 2 years. $__

36) $2,400 at 7% for 3 years. $__

37) $1,800 at 5% for 6 months. $__

38) $190 at 4% for 2 years. $__

39) $560 at 7% for 4 years. $__

40) $720 at 8% for 2 years. $_

41) $780 at 5% for 8 years. $__

42) $880 at 6% for 3 months. $__

Simple Interest - Answers

✎ *Determine the simple interest for following loans.*

1) $440 at 5% for 6 years. $132

2) $460 at 2.5% for 4 years. $46

3) $500 at 3% for 5 years. $75

4) $550 at 9% for 2 years. $99

5) $690 at 5% for 6 months. $17.25

6) $620 at 7% for 3 years. $130.20

7) $650 at 4.5% for 10 years. $292.50

8) $850 at 4% for 2 years. $68

9) $640 at 7% for 3 years. $134.40

10) $300 at 9% for 9 months. $20.25

11) $760 at 8% for 2 years. $121.60

12) $910 at 5% for 5 years. $227.50

13) $540 at 3% for 6 years. $97.20

14) $780 at 2.5% for 4 years. $78

15) $1,600 at 7% for 3 months. $28

16) $310 at 4% for 4 years. $49.60

17) $950 at 6% for 5 years. $285

18) $280 at 8% for 7 years. $156.80

19) $310 at 6% for 3 years. $55.80

20) $990 at 5% for 4 months. $198

21) $380 at 6% for 5 years. $114

22) $580 at 6% for 4 years. $139.20

23) $1,200 at 4% for 5 years. $240

24) $3,100 at 5% for 6 years. $930

25) $5,200 at 8% for 2 years. $832

26) $1,400 at 4% for 3 years. $168

27) $300 at 3% for 8 months. $6

28) $150 at 3.5% for 4 years. $21

29) $170 at 6% for 2 years. $20.40

30) $940 at 8% for 5 years. $376

31) $960 at 1.5% for 8 years. $115.20

32) $240 at 5% for 4 months. $4

33) $280 at 2% for 5 years. $28

34) $880 at 3% for 2 years. $52.80

35) $2,200 at 4.5% for 2 years. $198

36) $2,400 at 7% for 3 years. $504

37) $1,800 at 5% for 6 months. $45

38) $190 at 4% for 2 years. $15.20

39) $560 at 7% for 4 years. $156.80

40) $720 at 8% for 2 years. $115.20

41) $780 at 5% for 8 years. $312

42) $880 at 6% for 3 months. $13.20

Homework: #.....

Percent Problems

✍ *Solve each problem.*

1) What is 5 percent of 300? _____

2) What is 15 percent of 600? _____

3) What is 12 percent of 450? _____

4) What is 30 percent of 240? _____

5) What is 60 percent of 850? _____

6) 63 is what percent of 300? _____%

7) 80 is what percent of 400? _____%

8) 70 is what percent of 700? _____%

9) 84 is what percent of 600? ___%

10) 90 is what percent of 300? ___%

11) 24 is what percent of 150? ___%

12) 12 is what percent of 80? _____%

13) 4 is what percent of 50? _____%

14) 110 is what percent of 500? _%

15) 16 is what percent of 400? __%

16) 39 is what percent of 300? ___%

17) 56 is what percent of 200? ___%

18) 30 is what percent of 500? ___%

19) 84 is what percent of 700? ___%

20) 40 is what percent of 500? __%

21) 26 is what percent of 100? __ %

22) 45 is what percent of 900? __%

23) 60 is what percent of 400? ____%

24) 18 is what percent of 900? ____%

25) 75 is what percent of 250? ____%

26) 27 is what percent of 900? ____%

27) 49 is what percent of 700? ____%

28) 81 is what percent of 900? ____%

29) 90 is what percent of 500? ____%

30) 82 is 20 percent of what number? _____

31) 14 is 35 percent of what number? _____

32) 90 is 6 percent of what number? _____

33) 80 is 40 percent of what number? _____

34) 90 is 15 percent of what number? _____

35) 28 is 7 percent of what number? _____

36) 54 is 18 percent of what number? _____

37) 72 is 24 percent of what number? _____

Percent Problems - Answers

✎ *Solve each problem.*

1) What is 5 percent of 300? 15

2) What is 15 percent of 600? 90

3) What is 12 percent of 450? 54

4) What is 30 percent of 240? 72

5) What is 60 percent of 850? 510

6) 63 is what percent of 300? 21%

7) 80 is what percent of 400? 20%

8) 70 is what percent of 700? 10%

9) 84 is what percent of 600? 14%

10) 90 is what percent of 300? 30%

11) 24 is what percent of 150? 16%

12) 12 is what percent of 80? 15%

13) 4 is what percent of 50? 8%

14) 110 is what percent of 500? 22%

15) 16 is what percent of 400? 4%

16) 39 is what percent of 300? 13%

17) 56 is what percent of 200? 28%

18) 30 is what percent of 500? 6%

19) 84 is what percent of 700? 12%

20) 40 is what percent of 500? 8%

21) 26 is what percent of 100? 26%

22) 45 is what percent of 900? 5%

23) 60 is what percent of 400? 15%

24) 18 is what percent of 900? 2%

25) 75 is what percent of 250? 30%

26) 27 is what percent of 900? 3%

27) 49 is what percent of 700? 7%

28) 81 is what percent of 900? 9%

29) 90 is what percent of 500? 18%

30) 82 is 20 percent of what number? 410

31) 14 is 35 percent of what number? 40

32) 90 is 6 percent of what number? 1,500

33) 80 is 40 percent of what number? 200

34) 90 is 15 percent of what number? 600

35) 28 is 7 percent of what number? 400

36) 54 is 18 percent of what number? 300

37) 72 is 24 percent of what number? 300

Homework: #.....

Percent of Increase and Decrease

✍ *Solve each percent of change word problem.*

1) Bob got a raise, and his hourly wage increased from $24 to $36. What is the percent increase? _____ %

2) The price of gasoline rose from $2.20 to $2.42 in one month. By what percent did the gas price rise? _____ %

3) In a class, the number of students has been increased from 30 to 39. What is the percent increase? _____ %

4) The price of a pair of shoes increases from $28 to $35. What is the percent increase? ___ %

5) In a class, the number of students has been decreased from 24 to 18. What is the percentage decrease? _____ %

6) Nick got a raise, and his hourly wage increased from $50 to $55. What is the percent increase? _____ %

7) A coat was originally priced at $80. It went on sale for $70.40. What was the percent that the coat was discounted? _____ %

8) The price of a pair of shoes increases from $8 to $12. What is the percent increase? ___ %

9) A house was purchased in 2002 for $180,000. It is now valued at $144,000. What is the rate (percent) of depreciation for the house?_____ %

10) The price of gasoline rose from $3.00 to $3.15 in one month. By what percent did the gas price rise? _____ %

Homework: #.....

Percent of Increase and Decrease - Answers

✎ *Solve each percent of change word problem.*

1) Bob got a raise, and his hourly wage increased from $24 to $36. What is the percent increase? 50%

2) The price of gasoline rose from $2.20 to $2.42 in one month. By what percent did the gas price rise? 10%

3) In a class, the number of students has been increased from 30 to 39. What is the percent increase? 30%

4) The price of a pair of shoes increases from $28 to $35. What is the percent increase? 25%

5) In a class, the number of students has been decreased from 24 to 18. What is the percentage decrease? 25%

6) Nick got a raise, and his hourly wage increased from $50 to $55. What is the percent increase? 10%

7) A coat was originally priced at $80. It went on sale for $70.40. What was the percent that the coat was discounted? 12%

8) The price of a pair of shoes increases from $8 to $12. What is the percent increase? 50%

9) A house was purchased in 2002 for $180,000. It is now valued at $144,000. What is the rate (percent) of depreciation for the house? 20%

10) The price of gasoline rose from $3.00 to $3.15 in one month. By what percent did the gas price rise? 5%

Discount, Tax and Tip

✑ *Find the missing values.*

1) Original price of a computer: $400

   Tax: 5%, Selling price: $_____

2) Original price of a sofa: $600

   Tax: 12%, Selling price: $_____

3) Original price of a table: $550

   Tax: 18%, Selling price: $_____

4) Original price of a cell phone: $700

   Tax: 20%, Selling price: $_____

5) Original price of a printer: $400

   Tax: 22%, Selling price: $_____

6) Original price of a computer: $600

   Tax: 15%, Selling price: $_____

7) Restaurant bill: $24.00

   Tip: 25%, Final amount: $_____

8) Original price of a cell phone: $300

   Tax: 8%, Selling price: $_____

9) Original price of a carpet: $800

   Tax: 25%, Selling price: $_____

10) Original price of a camera: $200

    Discount: 35%, Selling price: $_____

11) Original price of a dress: $500

    Discount: 10%, Selling price: $_____

12) Original price of a monitor: $400

    Discount: 5%, Selling price: $_____

13) Original price of a laptop: $900

    Discount: 20%, Selling price: $_____

14) Restaurant bill: $54.00

    Tip: 20%, Final amount: $_____

Discount, Tax and Tip - Answers

✎ *Find the missing values.*

1) Original price of a computer: $400

Tax: 5%, Selling price: $420

2) Original price of a sofa: $600

Tax: 12%, Selling price: $672

3) Original price of a table: $550

Tax: 18%, Selling price: $649

4) Original price of a cell phone: $700

Tax: 20%, Selling price: $840

5) Original price of a printer: $400

Tax: 22%, Selling price: $488

6) Original price of a computer: $600

Tax: 15%, Selling price: $690

7) Restaurant bill: $24.00

Tip: 25%, Final amount: $30.00

8) Original price of a cell phone: $300

Tax: 8%, Selling price: $324

9) Original price of a carpet: $800

Tax: 25%, Selling price: $1,000

10) Original price of a camera: $200

Discount: 35%, Selling price: $130

11) Original price of a dress: $500

Discount: 10%, Selling price: $450

12) Original price of a monitor: $400

Discount: 5%, Selling price: $380

13) Original price of a laptop: $900

Discount: 20%, Selling price: $720

14) Restaurant bill: $54.00

Tip: 20%, Final amount: $64.80

Simplifying Variable Expressions

✎ *Simplify and write the answer.*

1) $3x + 5 + 2x =$

2) $7x + 3 - 3x =$

3) $-2 - x^2 - 6x^2 =$

4) $(-6)(8x - 4) =$

5) $3 + 10x^2 + 2x =$

6) $8x^2 + 6x + 7x^2 =$

7) $2x^2 - 5x - 7x =$

8) $x - 3 + 5 - 3x =$

9) $2 - 3x + 12 - 2x =$

10) $5x^2 - 12x^2 + 8x =$

11) $2x^2 + 6x + 3x^2 =$

12) $2x^2 - 2x - x =$

13) $2x^2 - (-8x + 6) = 2$

14) $4x + 6(2 - 5x) =$

15) $10x + 8(10x - 6) =$

16) $9(-2x - 6) - 5 =$

17) $32x - 4 + 23 + 2x =$

18) $8x - 12x - x^2 + 13 =$

19) $(-6)(8x - 4) + 10x =$

20) $14x - 5(5 - 8x) =$

21) $23x + 4(9x + 3) + 12 =$

22) $3(-7x + 5) + 20x =$

23) $12x - 3x(x + 9) =$

24) $7x + 5x(3 - 3x) =$

25) $5x(-8x + 12) + 14x =$

26) $40x + 12 + 2x^2 =$

27) $5x(x - 3) - 10 =$

28) $8x - 7 + 8x + 2x^2 =$

29) $7x - 3x^2 - 5x^2 - 3 =$

30) $4 + x^2 - 6x^2 - 12x =$

31) $12x + 8x^2 + 2x + 20 =$

32) $23 + 15x^2 + 8x - 4x^2 =$

Simplifying Variable Expressions - Answers

✎ *Simplify and write the answer.*

1) $3x + 5 + 2x = 5x + 5$

2) $7x + 3 - 3x = 4x + 3$

3) $-2 - x^2 - 6x^2 = -7x^2 - 2$

4) $(-6)(8x - 4) = -48x + 24$

5) $3 + 10x^2 + 2x = 10x^2 + 2x + 3$

6) $8x^2 + 6x + 7x^2 = 15x^2 + 6x$

7) $2x^2 - 5x - 7x = 2x^2 - 12x$

8) $x - 3 + 5 - 3x = -2x + 2$

9) $2 - 3x + 12 - 2x = -5x + 14$

10) $5x^2 - 12x^2 + 8x = -7x^2 + 8x$

11) $2x^2 + 6x + 3x^2 = 5x^2 + 6x$

12) $2x^2 - 2x - x = 2x^2 - 3x$

13) $2x^2 - (-8x + 6) = 2x^2 + 8x - 6$

14) $4x + 6(2 - 5x) = -26x + 12$

15) $10x + 8(10x - 6) = 90x - 48$

16) $9(-2x - 6) - 5 = -18x - 59$

17) $32x - 4 + 23 + 2x = 34x + 19$

18) $8x - 12x - x^2 + 13 = -x^2 - 4x + 13$

19) $(-6)(8x - 4) + 10x = -38x + 24$

20) $14x - 5(5 - 8x) = 54x - 25$

21) $23x + 4(9x + 3) + 12 = 59x + 24$

22) $3(-7x + 5) + 20x = -x + 15$

23) $12x - 3x(x + 9) = -3x^2 - 15x$

24) $7x + 5x(3 - 3x) = -15x^2 + 22x$

25) $5x(-8x + 12) + 14x = -40x^2 + 74x$

26) $40x + 12 + 2x^2 = 2x^2 + 40x + 12$

27) $5x(x - 3) - 10 = 5x^2 - 15x - 10$

28) $8x - 7 + 8x + 2x^2 = 2x^2 + 16x - 7$

29) $7x - 3x^2 - 5x^2 - 3 = -8x^2 + 7x - 3$

30) $4 + x^2 - 6x^2 - 12x = -5x^2 - 12x + 4$

31) $12x + 8x^2 + 2x + 20 = 8x^2 + 14x + 20$

32) $23 + 15x^2 + 8x - 4x^2 = 11x^2 + 8x + 23$

Simplifying Polynomial Expressions

✎ *Simplify and write the answer.*

1) $(2x^3 + 5x^2) - (12x + 2x^2) = $ _____ $2x^3 + 3x^2 - 12x$ _____

2) $(-x^5 + 2x^3) - (3x^3 + 6x^2) = $ _____

3) $(12x^4 + 4x^2) - (2x^2 - 6x^4) = $ _____

4) $4x - 3x^2 - 2(6x^2 + 6x^3) = $ _____

5) $(2x^3 - 3) + 3(2x^2 - 3x^3) = $ _____

6) $4(4x^3 - 2x) - (3x^3 - 2x^4) = $ _____

7) $2(4x - 3x^3) - 3(3x^3 + 4x^2) = $ _____

8) $(2x^2 - 2x) - (2x^3 + 5x^2) = $ _____

9) $2x^3 - (4x^4 + 2x) + x^2 = $ _____

10) $x^4 - 9(x^2 + x) - 5x = $ _____

11) $(-2x^2 - x^4) + (4x^4 - x^2) = $ _____

12) $4x^2 - 5x^3 + 15x^4 - 12x^3 = $ _____

13) $2x^2 - 5x^4 + 14x^4 - 11x^3 = $ _____

14) $2x^2 + 5x^3 - 7x^2 + 12x = $ _____

15) $2x^4 - 5x^5 + 8x^4 - 8x^2 = $ _____

16) $5x^3 + 17x - 5x^2 - 2x^3 = $ _____

Simplifying Polynomial Expressions - Answers

✎ *Simplify and write the answer.*

1) $(2x^3 + 5x^2) - (12x + 2x^2) = 2x^3 + 3x^2 - 12x$

2) $(-x^5 + 2x^3) - (3x^3 + 6x^2) = -x^5 - x^3 - 6x^2$

3) $(12x^4 + 4x^2) - (2x^2 - 6x^4) = 18x^4 + 2x^2$

4) $4x - 3x^2 - 2(6x^2 + 6x^3) = -12x^3 - 15x^2 + 4x$

5) $(2x^3 - 3) + 3(2x^2 - 3x^3) = -7x^3 + 6x^2 - 3$

6) $4(4x^3 - 2x) - (3x^3 - 2x^4) = 2x^4 + 13x^3 - 8x$

7) $2(4x - 3x^3) - 3(3x^3 + 4x^2) = -15x^3 - 12x^2 + 8x$

8) $(2x^2 - 2x) - (2x^3 + 5x^2) = -2x^3 - 3x^2 - 2x$

9) $2x^3 - (4x^4 + 2x) + x^2 = -4x^4 + 2x^3 + x^2 - 2x$

10) $x^4 - 9(x^2 + x) - 5x = x^4 - 9x^2 - 14x$

11) $(-2x^2 - x^4) + (4x^4 - x^2) = 3x^4 - 3x^2$

12) $4x^2 - 5x^3 + 15x^4 - 12x^3 = 15x^4 - 17x^3 + 4x^2$

13) $2x^2 - 5x^4 + 14x^4 - 11x^3 = 9x^4 - 11x^3 + 2x^2$

14) $2x^2 + 5x^3 - 7x^2 + 12x = 5x^3 - 5x^2 + 12x$

15) $2x^4 - 5x^5 + 8x^4 - 8x^2 = -5x^5 + 10x^4 - 8x^2$

16) $5x^3 + 17x - 5x^2 - 2x^3 = 3x^3 - 5x^2 + 17x$

Evaluating One Variable

✎ *Evaluate each expression using the value given.*

1) $x = 3 \Rightarrow 6x - 9 =$

2) $x = 2 \Rightarrow 7x - 10 =$

3) $x = 1 \Rightarrow 5x + 2 =$

4) $x = 2 \Rightarrow 3x + 9 =$

5) $x = 4 \Rightarrow 4x - 8 =$

6) $x = 2 \Rightarrow 5x - 2x + 10 =$

7) $x = 3 \Rightarrow 2x - x - 6 =$

8) $x = 4 \Rightarrow 6x - 3x + 4 =$

9) $x = -2 \Rightarrow 4x - 6x - 5 =$

10) $x = -1 \Rightarrow 3x - 5x + 11 =$

11) $x = 1 \Rightarrow x - 7x + 12 =$

12) $x = 2 \Rightarrow 2(-3x + 4) =$

13) $x = 3 \Rightarrow 4(-5x - 2) =$

14) $x = 2 \Rightarrow 5(-2x - 4) =$

15) $x = -2 \Rightarrow 3(-4x - 5) =$

16) $x = 3 \Rightarrow 8x + 5 =$

17) $x = -3 \Rightarrow 12x + 9 =$

18) $x = -1 \Rightarrow 9x - 8 =$

19) $x = 2 \Rightarrow 16x - 10 =$

20) $x = 1 \Rightarrow 4x + 3 =$

21) $x = 5 \Rightarrow 7x - 2 =$

22) $x = 7 \Rightarrow 28 - x =$

23) $x = 3 \Rightarrow 5x - 10 =$

24) $x = 12 \Rightarrow 40 - 2x =$

25) $x = 2 \Rightarrow 11x - 2 =$

26) $x = 3 \Rightarrow 2x - x + 10 =$

Evaluating One Variable - Answers

✎ Evaluate each expression using the value given.

1) $x = 3 \Rightarrow 6x - 9 = 9$

2) $x = 2 \Rightarrow 7x - 10 = 4$

3) $x = 1 \Rightarrow 5x + 2 = 7$

4) $x = 2 \Rightarrow 3x + 9 = 15$

5) $x = 4 \Rightarrow 4x - 8 = 8$

6) $x = 2 \Rightarrow 5x - 2x + 10 = 16$

7) $x = 3 \Rightarrow 2x - x - 6 = -3$

8) $x = 4 \Rightarrow 6x - 3x + 4 = 16$

9) $x = -2 \Rightarrow 4x - 6x - 5 = -1$

10) $x = -1 \Rightarrow 3x - 5x + 11 = 13$

11) $x = 1 \Rightarrow x - 7x + 12 = 6$

12) $x = 2 \Rightarrow 2(-3x + 4) = -4$

13) $x = 3 \Rightarrow 4(-5x - 2) = -68$

14) $x = 2 \Rightarrow 5(-2x - 4) = -40$

15) $x = -2 \Rightarrow 3(-4x - 5) = 9$

16) $x = 3 \Rightarrow 8x + 5 = 29$

17) $x = -3 \Rightarrow 12x + 9 = -27$

18) $x = -1 \Rightarrow 9x - 8 = -17$

19) $x = 2 \Rightarrow 16x - 10 = 22$

20) $x = 1 \Rightarrow 4x + 3 = 7$

21) $x = 5 \Rightarrow 7x - 2 = 33$

22) $x = 7 \Rightarrow 28 - x = 21$

23) $x = 3 \Rightarrow 5x - 10 = 5$

24) $x = 12 \Rightarrow 40 - 2x = 16$

25) $x = 2 \Rightarrow 11x - 2 = 20$

26) $x = 3 \Rightarrow 2x - x + 10 = 13$

Evaluating Two Variables

✎ *Evaluate each expression using the values given.*

1) $2x + 3y, x = 2, y = 3$

_____

2) $3x + 4y, x = -1, y = -2$

_____

3) $x + 6y, x = 3, y = 1$

_____

4) $2a - (15 - b), a = 2, b = 3$

_____

5) $4a - (6 - 3b), a = 1, b = 4$

_____

6) $a - (8 - 2b), a = 2, b = 5$

_____

7) $3z + 21 + 5k, z = 4, k = 1$

_____

8) $-7a + 4b, a = 6, b = 3$

_____

9) $-4a + 3b, a = 2, b = 4$

_____

10) $-6a + 6b, a = 4, b = 3$

_____

11) $-8a + 2b, a = 4, b = 6$

_____

12) $4x + 6y, x = 6, y = 3$

_____

13) $2x + 9y, x = 8, y = 1$

_____

14) $x - 7y, x = 9, y = 4$

_____

15) $5x - 4y, x = 6, y = 3$

_____

16) $2z + 14 + 8k, z = 4, k = 1$

_____

17) $6x + 3y, x = 3, y = 8$

_____

18) $5a - 6b, a = -3, b = -1$

_____

19) $8a + 4b, a = -4, b = 3$

_____

20) $-2a - b, a = 4, b = 9$

_____

21) $-7a + 3b, a = 4, b = 3$

_____

22) $-5a + 9b, a = 7, b = 1$

_____

Homework: #.....

Evaluating Two Variables - Answers

✎ *Evaluate each expression using the values given.*

1) $2x + 3y, x = 2, y = 3$
13

2) $3x + 4y, x = -1, y = -2$
-11

3) $x + 6y, x = 3, y = 1$
9

4) $2a - (15 - b), a = 2, b = 3$
-8

5) $4a - (6 - 3b), a = 1, b = 4$
10

6) $a - (8 - 2b), a = 2, b = 5$
4

7) $3z + 21 + 5k, z = 4, k = 1$
38

8) $-7a + 4b, a = 6, b = 3$
-30

9) $-4a + 3b, a = 2, b = 4$
4

10) $-6a + 6b, a = 4, b = 3$
-6

11) $-8a + 2b, a = 4, b = 6$
-20

12) $4x + 6y, x = 6, y = 3$
42

13) $2x + 9y, x = 8, y = 1$
25

14) $x - 7y, x = 9, y = 4$
-19

15) $5x - 4y, x = 6, y = 3$
18

16) $2z + 14 + 8k, z = 4, k = 1$
30

17) $6x + 3y, x = 3, y = 8$
42

18) $5a - 6b, a = -3, b = -1$
-9

19) $8a + 4b, a = -4, b = 3$
-20

20) $-2a - b, a = 4, b = 9$
-17

21) $-7a + 3b, a = 4, b = 3$
-19

22) $-5a + 9b, a = 7, b = 1$
-26

The Distributive Property

✍ *Use the distributive property to simply each expression.*

1) $(-3)(12x + 3) =$

2) $(-4x + 5)(-6) =$

3) $13(-4x + 2) =$

4) $7(6 - 3x) =$

5) $(6 - 5x)(-4) =$

6) $9(8 - 2x) =$

7) $(-4x + 6)5 =$

8) $(-2x + 7)(-8) =$

9) $8(-4x + 7) =$

10) $(-9x + 5)(-3) =$

11) $8(-x + 9) =$

12) $7(2 - 6x) =$

13) $(-12x + 4)(-3) =$

14) $(-6)(-10x + 6) =$

15) $(-5)(5 - 11x) =$

16) $9(4 - 8x) =$

17) $(-6x + 2)7 =$

18) $(-9)(1 - 12x) =$

19) $(-3)(4 - 6x) =$

20) $(2 - 8x)(-2) =$

21) $20(2 - x) =$

22) $12(-4x + 3) =$

23) $15(2 - 3x) =$

24) $(-4x + 5)2 =$

25) $(-11x + 8)(-2) =$

26) $14(5 - 8x) =$

The Distributive Property - Answers

🖎 *Use the distributive property to simply each expression.*

1) $(-3)(12x + 3) = -36x - 9$

2) $(-4x + 5)(-6) = 24x - 30$

3) $13(-4x + 2) = -52x + 26$

4) $7(6 - 3x) = -21x + 42$

5) $(6 - 5x)(-4) = 20x - 24$

6) $9(8 - 2x) = -18x + 72$

7) $(-4x + 6)5 = -20x + 30$

8) $(-2x + 7)(-8) = 16x - 56$

9) $8(-4x + 7) = -32x + 56$

10) $(-9x + 5)(-3) = 27x - 15$

11) $8(-x + 9) = -8x + 72$

12) $7(2 - 6x) = -42x + 14$

13) $(-12x + 4)(-3) = 36x - 12$

14) $(-6)(-10x + 6) = 60x - 36$

15) $(-5)(5 - 11x) = 55x - 25$

16) $9(4 - 8x) = -72x + 36$

17) $(-6x + 2)7 = -42x + 14$

18) $(-9)(1 - 12x) = 108x - 9$

19) $(-3)(4 - 6x) = 18x - 12$

20) $(2 - 8x)(-2) = 16x - 4$

21) $20(2 - x) = -20x + 40$

22) $12(-4x + 3) = -48x + 36$

23) $15(2 - 3x) = -45x + 30$

24) $(-4x + 5)2 = -8x + 10$

25) $(-11x + 8)(-2) = 22x - 16$

26) $14(5 - 8x) = -112x + 70$

Homework: #.....

One–Step Equations

✑ *Solve each equation for x.*

1) $x - 15 = 24 \Rightarrow x = $ ____

2) $18 = -6 + x \Rightarrow x = $ ___

3) $19 - x = 8 \Rightarrow x = $ ___

4) $x - 22 = 24 \Rightarrow x = $ ___

5) $24 - x = 17 \Rightarrow x = $ ___

6) $16 - x = 3 \Rightarrow x = $ ___

7) $x + 14 = 12 \Rightarrow x = $ ___

8) $26 + x = 8 \Rightarrow x = $ ___

9) $x + 9 = -18 \Rightarrow x = $ ___

10) $x + 21 = 11 \Rightarrow x = $ ___

11) $17 = -5 + x \Rightarrow x = $ ___

12) $x + 20 = 29 \Rightarrow x = $ ___

13) $x - 13 = 19 \Rightarrow x = $ ___

14) $x + 9 = -17 \Rightarrow x = $ ___

15) $x + 4 = -23 \Rightarrow x = $ ___

16) $16 = -9 + x \Rightarrow x = $ ___

17) $4x = 28 \Rightarrow x = $ ___

18) $21 = -7x \Rightarrow x = $ ___

19) $12x = -12 \Rightarrow x = $ ___

20) $13x = 39 \Rightarrow x = $ ___

21) $8x = -16 \Rightarrow x = $ ___

22) $\frac{x}{2} = -5 \Rightarrow x = $ ___

23) $\frac{x}{9} = 6 \Rightarrow x = $ ___

24) $27 = \frac{x}{5} \Rightarrow x = $ ___

25) $\frac{x}{4} = -3 \Rightarrow x = $ ___

26) $x \div 8 = 7 \Rightarrow x = $ ___

27) $x \div 2 = -3 \Rightarrow x = $ ___

28) $4x = 48 \Rightarrow x = $ ___

29) $9x = 72 \Rightarrow x = $ ___

30) $8x = -32 \Rightarrow x = $ ___

31) $80 = -10x \Rightarrow x = $ ___

One–Step Equations - Answers

✍ *Solve each equation for x.*

1) $x - 15 = 24 \Rightarrow x = 39$

2) $18 = -6 + x \Rightarrow x = 24$

3) $19 - x = 8 \Rightarrow x = 11$

4) $x - 22 = 24 \Rightarrow x = 46$

5) $24 - x = 17 \Rightarrow x = 7$

6) $16 - x = 3 \Rightarrow x = 13$

7) $x + 14 = 12 \Rightarrow x = 26$

8) $26 + x = 8 \Rightarrow x = -18$

9) $x + 9 = -18 \Rightarrow x = -27$

10) $x + 21 = 11 \Rightarrow x = -10$

11) $17 = -5 + x \Rightarrow x = 22$

12) $x + 20 = 29 \Rightarrow x = 9$

13) $x - 13 = 19 \Rightarrow x = 32$

14) $x + 9 = -17 \Rightarrow x = -26$

15) $x + 4 = -23 \Rightarrow x = -19$

16) $16 = -9 + x \Rightarrow x = 25$

17) $4x = 28 \Rightarrow x = 7$

18) $21 = -7x \Rightarrow x = -3$

19) $12x = -12 \Rightarrow x = -1$

20) $13x = 39 \Rightarrow x = 3$

21) $8x = -16 \Rightarrow x = -2$

22) $\frac{x}{2} = -5 \Rightarrow x = -10$

23) $\frac{x}{9} = 6 \Rightarrow x = 54$

24) $27 = \frac{x}{5} \Rightarrow x = 135$

25) $\frac{x}{4} = -3 \Rightarrow x = -12$

26) $x \div 8 = 7 \Rightarrow x = 56$

27) $x \div 2 = -3 \Rightarrow x = -6$

28) $4x = 48 \Rightarrow x = 12$

29) $9x = 72 \Rightarrow x = 8$

30) $8x = -32 \Rightarrow x = -4$

31) $80 = -10x \Rightarrow x = -8$

Multi –Step Equations

✎ *Solve each equation.*

1) $3x - 8 = 13 \Rightarrow x = $ ____

2) $23 = -(x - 5) \Rightarrow x = $ ____

3) $-(8 - x) = 15 \Rightarrow x = $ ____

4) $29 = -x + 12 \Rightarrow x = $ ____

5) $2(3 - 2x) = 10 \Rightarrow x = $ ____

6) $3x - 3 = 15 \Rightarrow x = $ ____

7) $32 = -x + 15 \Rightarrow x = $ ____

8) $-(10 - x) = -13 \Rightarrow x = $ ____

9) $-4(7 + x) = 4 \Rightarrow x = $ ____

10) $23 = 2x - 8 \Rightarrow x = $ ____

11) $-6(3 + x) = 6 \Rightarrow x = $ ____

12) $-3 = 3x - 15 \Rightarrow x = $ ____

13) $-7(12 + x) = 7 \Rightarrow x = $ ____

14) $8(6 - 4x) = 16 \Rightarrow x = $ ____

15) $18 - 4x = -9 - x \Rightarrow x = $ ____

16) $6(4 - x) = 30 \Rightarrow x = $ ____

17) $15 - 3x = -5 - x \Rightarrow x = $ ____

18) $9(-7 - 3x) = 18 \Rightarrow x = $ ____

19) $16 - 2x = -4 - 7x \Rightarrow x = $ ____

20) $14 - 2x = 14 + x \Rightarrow x = $ ____

21) $21 - 3x = -7 - 10x \Rightarrow x = $ ___

22) $8 - 2x = 11 + x \Rightarrow x = $ ____

23) $10 + 12x = -8 + 6x \Rightarrow x = $ ____

24) $25 + 20x = -5 + 5x \Rightarrow x = $ ____

25) $16 - x = -8 - 7x \Rightarrow x = $ ____

26) $17 - 3x = 13 + x \Rightarrow x = $ ____

27) $22 + 5x = -8 - x \Rightarrow x = $ ____

28) $-9(7 + x) = 9 \Rightarrow x = $ ____

29) $11 + 3x = -4 - 2x \Rightarrow x = $ ____

30) $13 - 2x = 3 - 3x \Rightarrow x = $ ____

31) $19 - x = -1 - 11x \Rightarrow x = $ ____

32) $12 - 2x = -2 - 4x \Rightarrow x = $ ____

Multi –Step Equations - Answers

✍ *Solve each equation.*

1) $3x - 8 = 13 \Rightarrow x = 7$

2) $23 = -(x - 5) \Rightarrow x = -18$

3) $-(8 - x) = 15 \Rightarrow x = 23$

4) $29 = -x + 12 \Rightarrow x = -17$

5) $2(3 - 2x) = 10 \Rightarrow x = -1$

6) $3x - 3 = 15 \Rightarrow x = 6$

7) $32 = -x + 15 \Rightarrow x = -17$

8) $-(10 - x) = -13 \Rightarrow x = -3$

9) $-4(7 + x) = 4 \Rightarrow x = -8$

10) $23 = 2x - 8 \Rightarrow x = 15$

11) $-6(3 + x) = 6 \Rightarrow x = -4$

12) $-3 = 3x - 15 \Rightarrow x = 4$

13) $-7(12 + x) = 7 \Rightarrow x = -13$

14) $8(6 - 4x) = 16 \Rightarrow x = 1$

15) $18 - 4x = -9 - x \Rightarrow x = 9$

16) $6(4 - x) = 30 \Rightarrow x = -1$

17) $15 - 3x = -5 - x \Rightarrow x = 10$

18) $9(-7 - 3x) = 18 \Rightarrow x = -3$

19) $16 - 2x = -4 - 7x \Rightarrow x = -4$

20) $14 - 2x = 14 + x \Rightarrow x = 0$

21) $21 - 3x = -7 - 10x \Rightarrow x = -4$

22) $8 - 2x = 11 + x \Rightarrow x = -1$

23) $10 + 12x = -8 + 6x \Rightarrow x = -3$

24) $25 + 20x = -5 + 5x \Rightarrow x = -2$

25) $16 - x = -8 - 7x \Rightarrow x = -4$

26) $17 - 3x = 13 + x \Rightarrow x = 1$

27) $22 + 5x = -8 - x \Rightarrow x = -5$

28) $-9(7 + x) = 9 \Rightarrow x = -8$

29) $11 + 3x = -4 - 2x \Rightarrow x = -3$

30) $13 - 2x = 3 - 3x \Rightarrow x = -10$

31) $19 - x = -1 - 11x \Rightarrow x = -2$

32) $12 - 2x = -2 - 4x \Rightarrow x = -7$

Graphing Single–Variable Inequalities

✎ *Graph each inequality.*

1) $x < 6$

2) $x \geq 1$

3) $x \geq -6$

4) $x \leq -2$

5) $x > -1$

6) $3 > x$

7) $2 \leq x$

8) $x > 0$

9) $-3 \leq x$

10) $-4 \leq x$

11) $x \leq 5$

12) $0 \leq x$

13) $-5 \leq x$

14) $x > -6$

Graphing Single–Variable Inequalities - Answers

✎ *Graph each inequality.*

1) $x < 6$

2) $x \geq 1$

3) $x \geq -6$

4) $x \leq -2$

5) $x > -1$

6) $3 > x$

7) $2 \leq x$

8) $x > 0$

9) $-3 \leq x$

10) $-4 \leq x$

11) $x \leq 5$

12) $0 \leq x$

13) $-5 \leq x$

14) $x > -6$

| Name: .... | Date: .... |

Homework: #.....

One–Step Inequalities

✍ *Solve each inequality for* x.

1) $x - 10 < 22 \Rightarrow$ _____

2) $18 \leq -4 + x \Rightarrow$ _____

3) $x - 33 > 8 \Rightarrow$ _____

4) $x + 22 \geq 24 \Rightarrow$ _____

5) $x - 24 > 17 \Rightarrow$ _____

6) $x + 5 \geq 3 \Rightarrow x$_____

7) $x + 14 < 12 \Rightarrow$ _____

8) $26 + x \leq 8 \Rightarrow$ _____

9) $x + 9 \geq -18 \Rightarrow$ _____

10) $x + 24 < 11 \Rightarrow$ _____

11) $17 \leq -5 + x \Rightarrow$ _____

12) $x + 25 > 29 \Rightarrow x$_____

13) $x - 17 \geq 19 \Rightarrow$ _____

14) $x + 8 > -17 \Rightarrow$ _____

15) $x + 8 < -23 \Rightarrow$ _____

16) $16 \leq -5 + x \Rightarrow$ _____

17) $4x \leq 12 \Rightarrow$ _____

18) $28 \geq -7x \Rightarrow$ _____

19) $2x > -14 \Rightarrow$ _____

20) $13x \leq 39 \Rightarrow$ _____

21) $-8x > -16 \Rightarrow$ _____

22) $\frac{x}{2} < -6 \Rightarrow$ _____

23) $\frac{x}{6} > 6 \Rightarrow$ _____

24) $27 \leq \frac{x}{4} \Rightarrow$ _____

25) $\frac{x}{8} < -3 \Rightarrow$ _____

26) $6x \geq 18 \Rightarrow$ _____

27) $5x \geq -25 \Rightarrow$ _____

28) $4x > 48 \Rightarrow$ _____

29) $8x \leq 72 \Rightarrow$ _____

30) $-4x < -32 \Rightarrow$ _____

31) $40 > -10x \Rightarrow$ _____

One–Step Inequalities - Answers

✍ *Solve each inequality for x.*

1) $x - 10 < 22 \Rightarrow x < 32$

2) $18 \leq -4 + x \Rightarrow 22 \leq x$

3) $x - 33 > 8 \Rightarrow 41 \leq x$

4) $x + 22 \geq 24 \Rightarrow x \geq 2$

5) $x - 24 > 17 \Rightarrow x > 41$

6) $x + 5 \geq 3 \Rightarrow x \geq -2$

7) $x + 14 < 12 \Rightarrow x < -2$

8) $26 + x \leq 8 \Rightarrow x \leq -18$

9) $x + 9 \geq -18 \Rightarrow x \geq -27$

10) $x + 24 < 11 \Rightarrow x < -13$

11) $17 \leq -5 + x \Rightarrow 22 \leq x$

12) $x + 25 > 29 \Rightarrow x > 4$

13) $x - 17 \geq 19 \Rightarrow x \geq 36$

14) $x + 8 > -17 \Rightarrow x > -25$

15) $x + 8 < -23 \Rightarrow x < -31$

16) $16 \leq -5 + x \Rightarrow 21 \leq x$

17) $4x \leq 12 \Rightarrow x \leq 3$

18) $28 \geq -7x \Rightarrow -4 \leq x$

19) $2x > -14 \Rightarrow x > -7$

20) $13x \leq 39 \Rightarrow x \leq 3$

21) $-8x > -16 \Rightarrow x < 2$

22) $\frac{x}{2} < -6 \Rightarrow x < -12$

23) $\frac{x}{6} > 6 \Rightarrow x > 36$

24) $27 \leq \frac{x}{4} \Rightarrow 108 \leq x$

25) $\frac{x}{8} < -3 \Rightarrow x < -24$

26) $6x \geq 18 \Rightarrow x \geq 3$

27) $5x \geq -25 \Rightarrow x \geq -5$

28) $4x > 48 \Rightarrow x > 12$

29) $8x \leq 72 \Rightarrow x \leq 9$

30) $-4x < -32 \Rightarrow x > 8$

31) $40 > -10x \Rightarrow -4 < x$

Multi –Step Inequalities

✎ *Solve each inequality.*

1) $2x - 8 \leq 8 \rightarrow$ _____

2) $3 + 2x \geq 17 \rightarrow$ _____

3) $5 + 3x \geq 26 \rightarrow$ _____

4) $2x - 8 \leq 14 \rightarrow$ _____

5) $3x - 4 \leq 23 \rightarrow$ _____

6) $7x - 5 \leq 51 \rightarrow$ _____

7) $4x - 9 \leq 27 \rightarrow$ _____

8) $6x - 11 \leq 13 \rightarrow$ _____

9) $5x - 7 \leq 33 \rightarrow$ _____

10) $6 + 2x \geq 28 \rightarrow$ _____

11) $8 + 3x \geq 35 \rightarrow$ _____

12) $4 + 6x < 34 \rightarrow$ _____

13) $3 + 2x \geq 53 \rightarrow$ _____

14) $7 - 6x > 56 + x \rightarrow$ _____

15) $9 + 4x \geq 39 + 2x \rightarrow$ _____

16) $3 + 5x \geq 43 \rightarrow$ _____

17) $4 - 7x < 60 \rightarrow$ _____

18) $11 - 4x \geq 55 \rightarrow$ _____

19) $12 + x \geq 48 - 2x \rightarrow$ _____

20) $10 - 10x \leq -20 \rightarrow$ _____

21) $5 - 9x \geq -40 \rightarrow$ _____

22) $8 - 7x \geq 36 \rightarrow$ _____

23) $5 + 11x < 69 + 3x \rightarrow$ _____

24) $6 + 8x < 28 - 3x \rightarrow$ _____

25) $9 + 11x < 57 - x \rightarrow$ _____

26) $3 + 10x \geq 45 - 4x \rightarrow$ _____

| Name: .... | Date: .... |

Homework: #.....

Multi –Step Inequalities - Answers

✍ *Solve each inequality.*

1) $2x - 8 \leq 8 \rightarrow x \leq 8$

2) $3 + 2x \geq 17 \rightarrow x \geq 7$

3) $5 + 3x \geq 26 \rightarrow x \geq 7$

4) $2x - 8 \leq 14 \rightarrow x \leq 11$

5) $3x - 4 \leq 23 \rightarrow x \leq 9$

6) $7x - 5 \leq 51 \rightarrow x \leq 8$

7) $4x - 9 \leq 27 \rightarrow x \leq 9$

8) $6x - 11 \leq 13 \rightarrow x \leq 4$

9) $5x - 7 \leq 33 \rightarrow x \leq 8$

10) $6 + 2x \geq 28 \rightarrow x \geq 11$

11) $8 + 3x \geq 35 \rightarrow x \geq 9$

12) $4 + 6x < 34 \rightarrow x < 5$

13) $3 + 2x \geq 53 \rightarrow x \geq 25$

14) $7 - 6x > 56 + x \rightarrow x < -7$

15) $9 + 4x \geq 39 + 2x \rightarrow x \geq 15$

16) $3 + 5x \geq 43 \rightarrow x \geq 8$

17) $4 - 7x < 60 \rightarrow x > -8$

18) $11 - 4x \geq 55 \rightarrow x \leq -11$

19) $12 + x \geq 48 - 2x \rightarrow x \geq 12$

20) $10 - 10x \leq -20 \rightarrow x \geq 3$

21) $5 - 9x \geq -40 \rightarrow x \leq 5$

22) $8 - 7x \geq 36 \rightarrow x \leq -4$

23) $5 + 11x < 69 + 3x \rightarrow x < 8$

24) $6 + 8x < 28 - 3x \rightarrow x < 2$

25) $9 + 11x < 57 - x \rightarrow x < 4$

26) $3 + 10x \geq 45 - 4x \rightarrow x \geq 3$

Homework: #.....

System of Equations

✎ *Solve each system of equations.*

1) $-x + y = 2$ $x =$

    $-2x + y = 3$ $y =$

2) $-5x + y = -3$ $x =$

    $3x - 8y = 24$ $y =$

3) $y = -5$ $x =$

    $4x - 5y = 13$

4) $3y = -6x + 8$ $x =$

    $5x - 4y = -3$ $y =$

5) $10x - 8y = -15$ $x =$

    $-6x + 4y = 13$ $y =$

6) $-3x - 4y = 5$ $x =$

    $x - 2y = 5$ $y =$

7) $5x - 12y = -19$ $x =$

    $-6x + 7y = 8$ $y =$

8) $5x - 7y = -2$ $x =$

    $-x - 2y = -3$ $y =$

9) $-x + 3y = 3$ $x =$

    $-7x + 8y = -5$ $y =$

10) $-4x + 3y = -18$ $x =$

    $4x - y = 14$ $y =$

11) $6x - 7y = -8$ $x =$

    $-x - 4y = -9$ $y =$

12) $-3x + 2y = -16$ $x =$

    $4x - y = 13$ $y =$

System of Equations- Answers

✎ *Solve each system of equations.*

1) $-x + y = 2$ $x = -1$

     $-2x + y = 3$ $y = 1$

2) $-5x + y = -3$ $x = 0$

     $3x - 8y = 24$ $y = -3$

3) $y = -5$ $x = -3$

     $4x - 5y = 13$

4) $y = -6x + 8$ $x = 1$

     $5x - 4y = -3$ $y = 2$

5) $10x - 8y = -15$ $x = -\dfrac{11}{2}$

     $-6x + 4y = 13$ $y = -5$

6) $-3x - 4y = 5$ $x = 1$

     $x - 2y = 5$ $y = -2$

7) $5x - 12y = -19$ $x = 1$

     $-6x + 7y = 8$ $y = 2$

8) $5x - 7y = -2$ $x = 1$

     $-x - 3y = -3$ $y = 1$

9) $-x + 3y = 3$ $x = 3$

     $-7x + 8y = -5$ $y = 2$

10) $-4x + 3y = -18$ $x = 3$

     $4x - y = 14$ $y = -2$

11) $6x - 7y = -8$ $x = 1$

     $-x - 4y = -9$ $y = 2$

12) $-3x + 2y = -16$ $x = 2$

     $4x - y = 13$ $y = -5$

Homework: #.....

Finding Slope

✍ *Find the slope of each line.*

1) $y = x - 5$, Slope =

2) $y = -3x + 2$, Slope =

3) $y = -x - 1$, Slope =

4) $y = -x - 9$, Slope =

5) $y = 5 + 2x$, Slope =

6) $y = 1 - 8x$, Slope =

7) $y = -4x + 3$, Slope =

8) $y = -9x + 8$, Slope =

9) $y = -2x + 4$, Slope =

10) $y = 9x - 8$, Slope =

11) $y = \frac{1}{2}x + 4$, Slope =

12) $y = -\frac{2}{5}x + 7$, Slope =

13) $-x + 3y = 5$, Slope =

14) $4x + 4y = 6$, Slope =

15) $6y - 2x = 10$, Slope =

16) $3y - x = 2$, Slope =

✍ *Find the slope of the line through each pair of points.*

1) $(4, 4), (8, 12)$, Slope =

7) $(8, 4), (9, 6)$, Slope =

2) $(-2, 4), (0, 6)$, Slope =

8) $(10, -1), (7, 8)$, Slope =

3) $(6, -2), (2, 6)$, Slope =

9) $(14, -7), (13, -6)$, Slope =

4) $(-4, -2), (0, 6)$, Slope =

10) $(10, 7), (8, 1)$, Slope =

5) $(6, 2), (3, 5)$, Slope =

11) $(5, 1), (8, 10)$, Slope =

6) $(-5, 1), (-1, 9)$, Slope =

1) $(9, -10), (8, 12)$, Slope =

Homework: #.....

Finding Slope - Answers

✎ *Find the slope of each line.*

1) $y = x - 5$, Slope $= 1$

2) $y = -3x + 2$, Slope $= -3$

3) $y = -x - 1$, Slope $= -1$

4) $y = -x - 9$, Slope $= -1$

5) $y = 5 + 2x$, Slope $= 2$

6) $y = 1 - 8x$, Slope $= -8$

7) $y = -4x + 3$, Slope $= -4$

8) $y = -9x + 8$, Slope $= -9$

9) $y = -2x + 4$, Slope $= -2$

10) $y = 9x - 8$, Slope $= 9$

11) $y = \frac{1}{2}x + 4$, Slope $= \frac{1}{2}$

12) $y = -\frac{2}{5}x + 7$, Slope $= -\frac{2}{5}$

13) $-x + 3y = 5$, Slope $= \frac{1}{3}$

14) $4x + 4y = 6$, Slope $= -1$

15) $6y - 2x = 10$, Slope $= \frac{1}{3}$

16) $3y - x = 2$, Slope $= \frac{1}{3}$

✎ *Find the slope of the line through each pair of points.*

1) $(4, 4), (8, 12)$, Slope $= 2$

7) $(8, 4), (9, 6)$, Slope $= 2$

2) $(-2, 4), (0, 6)$, Slope $= 1$

8) $(10, -1), (7, 8)$, Slope $= -3$

3) $(6, -2), (2, 6)$, Slope $= -2$

9) $(14, -7), (13, -6)$, Slope $= -1$

4) $(-4, -2), (0, 6)$, Slope $= 2$

10) $(10, 7), (8, 1)$, Slope $= 3$

5) $(6, 2), (3, 5)$, Slope $= -1$

11) $(5, 1), (8, 10)$, Slope $= 3$

6) $(-5, 1), (-1, 9)$, Slope $= 2$

12) $(9, -10), (8, 12)$, Slope $= -22$

78

Homework: #.....

Graphing Lines Using Slope–Intercept Form

✍ *Sketch the graph of each line.*

1) $y = -x + 1$

2) $y = 2x - 3$

3) $y = -x + 2$

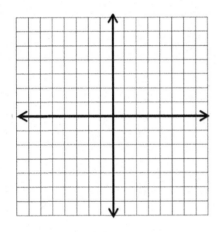
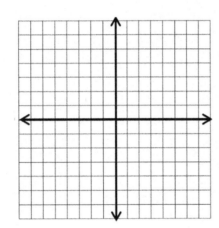
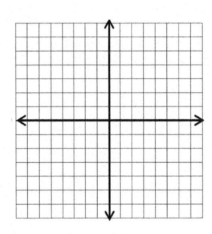

4) $y = x + 1$

5) $y = 2x - 4$

6) $y = -\frac{1}{2}x + 1$

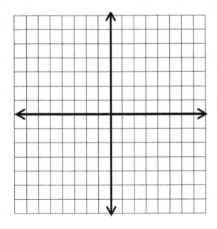
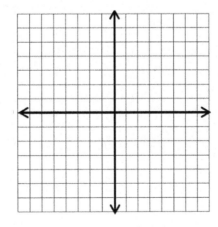
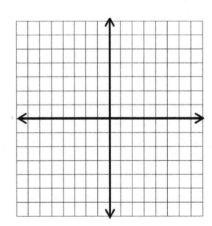

Graphing Lines Using Slope–Intercept Form - Answers

✍ *Sketch the graph of each line.*

1) $y = -x + 1$

2) $y = 2x - 3$

3) $y = -x + 2$

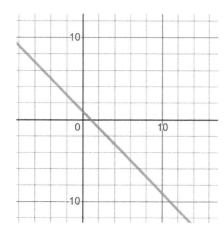

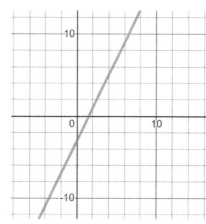

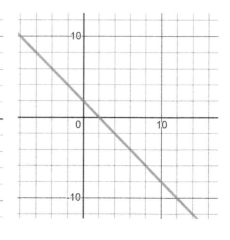

4) $y = x + 1$

5) $y = 2x - 4$

6) $y = -\frac{1}{2}x + 1$

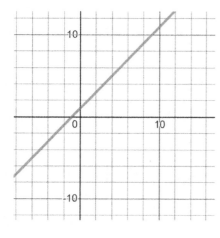

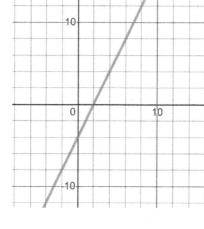

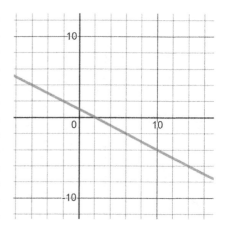

Writing Linear Equations

✎ *Write the equation of the line through the given points.*

1) through: $(1, -2), (2, 4)$

$y =$

2) through: $(-2, 3), (1, 6)$

$y =$

3) through: $(-1, 2), (3, 6)$

$y =$

4) through: $(8, 5), (5, 2)$

$y =$

5) through: $(7, -10), (2, 10)$

$y =$

6) through: $(7, 2), (6, 1)$

$y =$

7) through: $(6, -1), (4, 1)$

$y =$

8) through: $(-2, 8), (-4, -6)$

$y =$

9) through: $(-2, 5), (-3, 4)$

$y =$

10) through: $(6, 8), (8, -6)$

$y =$

11) through: $(-2, 5), (-4, -3)$

$y =$

12) through: $(8, 8), (4, -8)$

$y =$

13) through: $(7, -4)$, Slope: -1

$y =$

14) through: $(4, -10)$, Slope: -2

$y =$

15) through: $(6, 10)$, Slope: 9

$y =$

16) through: $(-6, 8)$, Slope: -2

$y =$

✎ *Solve each problem.*

17) What is the equation of a line with slope 8 and intercept 5? _____

18) What is the equation of a line with slope 4 and intercept 10? _____

19) What is the equation of a line with slope 9 and passes through point $(5, 23)$?

_____

20) What is the equation of a line with slope -7 and passes through point $(-3, 18)$?

_____

Homework: #.....

Writing Linear Equations - Answers

✍ *Write the equation of the line through the given points.*

1) through: $(1, -2), (2, 4)$

   $y = 6x - 8$

2) through: $(-2, 3), (1, 6)$

   $y = x + 5$

3) through: $(-1, 2), (3, 6)$

   $y = x + 3$

4) through: $(8, 5), (5, 2)$

   $y = x - 3$

5) through: $(7, -10), (2, 10)$

   $y = -4x + 18$

6) through: $(7, 2), (6, 1)$

   $y = x - 5$

7) through: $(6, -1), (4, 1)$

   $y = -x + 5$

8) through: $(-2, 8), (-4, -6)$

   $y = 7x + 22$

9) through: $(-2, 5), (-3, 4)$

   $y = x + 7$

10) through: $(6, 8), (8, -6)$

    $y = -7x + 50$

11) through: $(-2, 5), (-4, -3)$

    $y = 4x + 13$

12) through: $(8, 8), (4, -8)$

    $y = 4x - 24$

13) through: $(7, -4)$, Slope: -1

    $y = -x + 3$

14) through: $(4, -10)$, Slope: -2

    $y = -2x - 2$

15) through: $(6, 10)$, Slope: 9

    $y = 9x - 44$

16) through: $(-6, 8)$, Slope: -2

    $y = -2x - 4$

✍ *Solve each problem.*

17) What is the equation of a line with slope 8 and intercept 5? $y = 8x + 5$

18) What is the equation of a line with slope 4 and intercept 10? $y = 4x + 10$

19) What is the equation of a line with slope 9 and passes through point $(5, 23)$?

   $y = 9x - 22$

20) What is the equation of a line with slope -7 and passes through point $(-3, 18)$?

   $y = -7x - 3$

Finding Midpoint

✎ *Find the midpoint of the line segment with the given endpoints.*

1) $(2,2), (0,4)$,

$midpoint = (\underline{}, \underline{})$

2) $(3,3), (-1,5)$,

$midpoint = (\underline{}, \underline{})$

3) $(2,-1), (0,5)$,

$midpoint = (\underline{}, \underline{})$

4) $(-3,7), (-1,5)$,

$midpoint = (\underline{}, \underline{})$

5) $(5,-2), (9,-6)$,

$midpoint = (\underline{}, \underline{})$

6) $(-6,-3), (4,-7)$,

$midpoint = (\underline{}, \underline{})$

7) $(7,0), (-7,8)$,

$midpoint = (\underline{}, \underline{})$

8) $(-8,4), (-4,0)$,

$midpoint = (\underline{}, \underline{})$

9) $(-3,6), (9,-8)$,

$midpoint = (\underline{}, \underline{})$

10) $(6,8), (6,-6)$,

$midpoint = (\underline{}, \underline{})$

11) $(6,7), (-8,5)$,

$midpoint = (\underline{}, \underline{})$

12) $(9,3), (-3,-9)$,

$midpoint = (\underline{}, \underline{})$

13) $(-6,12), (-4,6)$,

$midpoint = (\underline{}, \underline{})$

14) $(10,7), (8,-3)$,

$midpoint = (\underline{}, \underline{})$

15) $(13,7), (-5,3)$,

$midpoint = (\underline{}, \underline{})$

16) $(-9,-4), (-5,8)$,

$midpoint = (\underline{}, \underline{})$

17) $(11,7), (5,13)$,

$midpoint = (\underline{}, \underline{})$

18) $(-7,-10), (11,-2)$,

$midpoint = (\underline{}, \underline{})$

19) $(10,15), (-4,9)$,

$midpoint = (\underline{}, \underline{})$

20) $(11,-4), (7,12)$,

$midpoint = (\underline{}, \underline{})$

Finding Midpoint - Answers

✎ *Find the midpoint of the line segment with the given endpoints.*

1) $(2, 2), (0, 4),$
   $midpoint = (1, 3)$

2) $(3, 3), (-1, 5),$
   $midpoint = (1, 4)$

3) $(2, -1), (0, 5),$
   $midpoint = (1, 2)$

4) $(-3, 7), (-1, 5),$
   $midpoint = (-2, 6)$

5) $(5, -2), (9, -6),$
   $midpoint = (7, -4)$

6) $(-6, -3), (4, -7),$
   $midpoint = (-1, -5)$

7) $(7, 0), (-7, 8),$
   $midpoint = (0, 4)$

8) $(-8, 4), (-4, 0),$
   $midpoint = (-6, 2)$

9) $(-3, 6), (9, -8),$
   $midpoint = (3, -1)$

10) $(6, 8), (6, -6),$
   $midpoint = (6, 1)$

11) $(6, 7), (-8, 5),$
   $midpoint = (-1, 6)$

12) $(9, 3), (-3, -9),$
   $midpoint = (3, -3)$

13) $(-6, 12), (-4, 6),$
   $midpoint = (-5, 9)$

14) $(10, 7), (8, -3),$
   $midpoint = (9, 2)$

15) $(13, 7), (-5, 3),$
   $midpoint = (4, 5)$

16) $(-9, -4), (-5, 8),$
   $midpoint = (-7, 2)$

17) $(11, 7), (5, 13),$
   $midpoint = (8, 10)$

18) $(-7, -10), (11, -2),$
   $midpoint = (2, -6)$

19) $(10, 15), (-4, 9),$
   $midpoint = (3, 12)$

20) $(11, -4), (7, 12),$
   $midpoint = (9, 4)$

Homework: #.....

Finding Distance of Two Points

✍ *Find the distance of each pair of points.*

1) $(1, 9), (5, 6),$

   Distance = ____

2) $(-4, 5), (8, 10),$

   Distance = ____

3) $(5, -2), (-3, 4),$

   Distance = ____

4) $(-3, 0), (3, 8),$

   Distance = ____

5) $(-5, 3), (4, -9),$

   Distance = ____

6) $(-7, -5), (5, 0),$

   Distance = ____

7) $(4, 3), (-4, -12),$

   Distance = ____

8) $(10, 1), (-5, -19),$

   Distance = ____

9) $(3, 3), (-1, 5),$

   Distance = ____

10) $(2, -1), (10, 5),$

    Distance = ____

11) $(-3, 7), (-1, 4),$

    Distance = ____

12) $(5, -2), (9, -5),$

    Distance = ____

13) $(-8, 4), (4, 9),$

    Distance = ____

14) $(6, 8), (6, -6),$

    Distance = ____

15) $(9, 3), (-3, -2),$

    Distance = ____

16) $(-4, 12), (-4, 6),$

    Distance = ____

17) $(-9, -4), (-4, 8),$

    Distance = ____

18) $(11, 7), (3, 22),$

    Distance = ____

Finding Distance of Two Points - Answers

✎ *Find the distance of each pair of points.*

1) $(1, 9), (5, 6)$,

   Distance $= 5$

2) $(-4, 5), (8, 10)$,

   Distance $= 13$

3) $(5, -2), (-3, 4)$,

   Distance $= 10$

4) $(-3, 0), (3, 8)$,

   Distance $= 10$

5) $(-5, 3), (4, -9)$,

   Distance $= 15$

6) $(-7, -5), (5, 0)$,

   Distance $= 13$

7) $(4, 3), (-4, -12)$,

   Distance $= 17$

8) $(10, 1), (-5, -19)$,

   Distance $= 25$

9) $(3, 3), (-1, 5)$,

   Distance $= \sqrt{20} = 2\sqrt{5}$

10) $(2, -1), (10, 5)$,

    Distance $= 10$

11) $(-3, 7), (-1, 4)$,

    Distance $= 5$

12) $(5, -2), (9, -5)$,

    Distance $= 5$

13) $(-8, 4), (4, 9)$,

    Distance $= 13$

14) $(6, 8), (6, -6)$,

    Distance $= 14$

15) $(9, 3), (-3, -2)$,

    Distance $= 13$

16) $(-4, 12), (-4, 6)$,

    Distance $= 6$

17) $(-9, -4), (-4, 8)$,

    Distance $= 13$

18) $(11, 7), (3, 22)$,

    Distance $= 17$

Homework: #.....

Multiplication Property of Exponents

✍ *Simplify and write the answer in exponential form.*

1) $2 \times 2^2 =$

2) $5^3 \times 5 =$

3) $3^2 \times 3^2 =$

4) $4^2 \times 4^2 =$

5) $7^3 \times 7^2 \times 7 =$

6) $2 \times 2^2 \times 2^2 =$

7) $5^3 \times 5^2 \times 5 \times 5 =$

8) $2x \times x =$

9) $x^3 \times x^2 =$

10) $x^4 \times x^4 =$

11) $x^2 \times x^2 \times x^2 =$

12) $6x \times 6x =$

13) $2x^2 \times 2x^2 =$

14) $3x^2 \times x =$

15) $4x^4 \times 4x^4 \times 4x^4 =$

16) $2x^2 \times x^2 =$

17) $x^4 \times 3x =$

18) $x \times 2x^2 =$

19) $5x^4 \times 5x^4 =$

20) $2yx^2 \times 2x =$

21) $3x^4 \times y^2x^4 =$

22) $y^2x^3 \times y^5x^2 =$

23) $4yx^3 \times 2x^2y^3 =$

24) $6x^2 \times 6x^3y^4 =$

25) $3x^4y^5 \times 7x^2y^3 =$

26) $7x^2y^5 \times 9xy^3 =$

27) $7xy^4 \times 4x^3y^3 =$

28) $3x^5y^3 \times 8x^2y^3 =$

29) $3x \times y^5x^3 \times y^4 =$

30) $yx^2 \times 2y^2x^2 \times 2xy =$

31) $4yx^4 \times 5y^5x \times xy^3 =$

32) $7x^2 \times 10x^3y^3 \times 8yx^4 =$

Name: ....

Date: ....

Homework: #.....

Multiplication Property of Exponents - Answers

✎ *Simplify and write the answer in exponential form.*

1) $2 \times 2^2 = 2^3$

2) $5^3 \times 5 = 5^4$

3) $3^2 \times 3^2 = 3^4$

4) $4^2 \times 4^2 = 4^4$

5) $7^3 \times 7^2 \times 7 = 7^6$

6) $2 \times 2^2 \times 2^2 = 2^5$

7) $5^3 \times 5^2 \times 5 \times 5 = 5^7$

8) $2x \times x = 2x^2$

9) $x^3 \times x^2 = x^5$

10) $x^4 \times x^4 = x^8$

11) $x^2 \times x^2 \times x^2 = x^6$

12) $6x \times 6x = 36x^2$

13) $2x^2 \times 2x^2 = 4x^4$

14) $3x^2 \times x = 3x^3$

15) $4x^4 \times 4x^4 \times 4x^4 = 64x^{12}$

16) $2x^2 \times x^2 = 2x^4$

17) $x^4 \times 3x = 3x^5$

18) $x \times 2x^2 = 2x^3$

19) $5x^4 \times 5x^4 = 25x^8$

20) $2yx^2 \times 2x = 4x^3 y$

21) $3x^4 \times y^2 x^4 = 3x^8 y^2$

22) $y^2 x^3 \times y^5 x^2 = x^5 y^7$

23) $4yx^3 \times 2x^2 y^3 = 8x^5 y^4$

24) $6x^2 \times 6x^3 y^4 = 36x^5 y^4$

25) $3x^4 y^5 \times 7x^2 y^3 = 21x^6 y^8$

26) $7x^2 y^5 \times 9xy^3 = 63x^3 y^8$

27) $7xy^4 \times 4x^3 y^3 = 28x^4 y^7$

28) $3x^5 y^3 \times 8x^2 y^3 = 24x^7 y^6$

29) $3x \times y^5 x^3 \times y^4 = 3x^4 y^9$

30) $yx^2 \times 2y^2 x^2 \times 2xy = 4x^5 y^4$

31) $4yx^4 \times 5y^5 x \times xy^3 = 20x^6 y^9$

32) $7x^2 \times 10x^3 y^3 \times 8yx^4 = 560x^9 y^4$

Division Property of Exponents

✎ *Simplify and write the answer.*

1) $\dfrac{2^2}{2^3} =$

2) $\dfrac{2^4}{2^2} =$

3) $\dfrac{5^5}{5} =$

4) $\dfrac{3}{3^5} =$

5) $\dfrac{x}{x^3} =$

6) $\dfrac{3 \times 3^3}{3^2 \times 3^4} =$

7) $\dfrac{5^8}{5^3} =$

8) $\dfrac{5 \times 5^6}{5^2 \times 5^7} =$

9) $\dfrac{3^4 \times 3^7}{3^2 \times 3^8} =$

10) $\dfrac{5x}{10^{\ 3}} =$

11) $\dfrac{5x^3}{2x^5} =$

12) $\dfrac{18^{\ 3}}{14x^6} =$

13) $\dfrac{12^{\ 3}}{8xy^8} =$

14) $\dfrac{24xy^3}{4x^4y^2} =$

15) $\dfrac{21x^3y^9}{7xy^5} =$

16) $\dfrac{36^{\ 2}y^9}{4x^3} =$

17) $\dfrac{12x^4y^4}{10^{\ 6}y^7} =$

18) $\dfrac{12y^2x^{12}}{20yx^8} =$

19) $\dfrac{16^{\ 4}y}{9x^8y^2} =$

20) $\dfrac{5x^8y^2}{20x^5y^5} =$

Division Property of Exponents - Answers

🖎 *Simplify and write the answer.*

1) $\dfrac{2^2}{2^3} = \dfrac{1}{2}$

2) $\dfrac{2^4}{2^2} = 2^2$

3) $\dfrac{5^5}{5} = 5^4$

4) $\dfrac{3}{3^5} = \dfrac{1}{3^4}$

5) $\dfrac{x}{x^3} = \dfrac{1}{x^2}$

6) $\dfrac{3^3}{3^4} = \dfrac{1}{3}$

7) $\dfrac{5^8}{5^3} = 5^5$

8) $\dfrac{5 \times 5^6}{5^2 \times 5^7} = \dfrac{1}{5^2}$

9) $\dfrac{3^4 \times 3^7}{3^2 \times 3^8} = 3$

10) $\dfrac{5x}{10x^3} = \dfrac{1}{2x^2}$

11) $\dfrac{5x^3}{2x^5} = \dfrac{5}{2x^2}$

12) $\dfrac{18x^3}{14x^6} = \dfrac{9}{7x^3}$

13) $\dfrac{12x^3}{8xy^8} = \dfrac{3x^2}{2y^8}$

14) $\dfrac{24xy^3}{4x^4y^2} = \dfrac{6y}{x^3}$

15) $\dfrac{21x^3y^9}{7xy^5} = 3x^2y^4$

16) $\dfrac{36x^2y^9}{4x^3} = \dfrac{9y^9}{x}$

17) $\dfrac{12^{\,4}y^4}{10x^6y^7} = \dfrac{6}{5x^2y^3}$

18) $\dfrac{12y^2x^{12}}{20yx^8} = \dfrac{3yx^4}{5}$

19) $\dfrac{16^{\,4}y}{9x^8y^2} = \dfrac{16}{9x^4y}$

20) $\dfrac{5x^8y^2}{20^{\,5}y^5} = \dfrac{x^3}{4y^3}$

Homework: #.....

Powers of Products and Quotients

✎ *Simplify and write the answer.*

1) $(4^2)^2 =$

2) $(6^2)^3 =$

3) $(2 \times 2^3)^4 =$

4) $(4 \times 4^4)^2 =$

5) $(3^3 \times 3^2)^3 =$

6) $(5^4 \times 5^5)^2 =$

7) $(2 \times 2^4)^2 =$

8) $(2x^6)^2 =$

9) $(11x^5)^2 =$

10) $(4x^2y^4)^4 =$

11) $(2x^4y^4)^3 =$

12) $(3x^2y^2)^2 =$

13) $(3x^4y^3)^4 =$

14) $(2x^6y^8)^2 =$

15) $(12x^3x)^3 =$

16) $(5x^9x^6)^3 =$

17) $(5x^{10}y^3)^3 =$

18) $(14x^3x^3)^2 =$

19) $(3x^3.5x)^2 =$

20) $(10x^{11}y^3)^2 =$

21) $(9x^7y^5)^2 =$

22) $(4x^4y^6)^5 =$

23) $(3x \cdot 4y^3)^2 =$

24) $\left(\frac{6x}{x^2}\right)^2 =$

25) $\left(\frac{x^5y^5}{x^2y^2}\right)^3 =$

26) $\left(\frac{24x}{4x^6}\right)^2 =$

27) $\left(\frac{x^5}{x^7y^2}\right)^2 =$

28) $\left(\frac{xy^2}{x^2y^3}\right)^3 =$

29) $\left(\frac{4xy^4}{x^5}\right)^2 =$

30) $\left(\frac{xy^4}{5xy^2}\right)^3 =$

Powers of Products and Quotients - Answers

✎ *Simplify and write the answer.*

1) $(4^2)^2 = 4^4$

2) $(6^2)^3 = 6^6$

3) $(2 \times 2^3)^4 = 2^{16}$

4) $(4 \times 4^4)^2 = 4^{10}$

5) $(3^3 \times 3^2)^3 = 3^{15}$

6) $(5^4 \times 5^5)^2 = 5^{18}$

7) $(2 \times 2^4)^2 = 2^{10}$

8) $(2x^6)^2 = 4x^{12}$

9) $(11x^5)^2 = 121x^{10}$

10) $(4x^2y^4)^4 = 256x^8y^{16}$

11) $(2x^4y^4)^3 = 8x^{12}y^{12}$

12) $(3x^2y^2)^2 = 9x^4y^4$

13) $(3x^4y^3)^4 = 81x^{16}y^{12}$

14) $(2x^6y^8)^2 = 4x^{12}y^{16}$

15) $(12x^3x)^3 = 1,728x^{12}$

16) $(5x^9x^6)^3 = 125x^{45}$

17) $(5x^{10}y^3)^3 = 125x^{30}y^9$

18) $(14x^3x^3)^2 = 196x^{12}$

19) $(3x^3 . 5x)^2 = 225x^8$

20) $(10x^{11}y^3)^2 = 100x^{22}y^6$

21) $(9x^7y^5)^2 = 81x^{14}y^{10}$

22) $(4x^4y^6)^5 = 1,024x^{20}y^{30}$

23) $(3x . 4y^3)^2 = 144x^2y^6$

24) $\left(\frac{6x}{x^2}\right)^2 = \frac{36}{x^2}$

25) $\left(\frac{x^5y^5}{x^2y^2}\right)^3 = x^9y^9$

26) $\left(\frac{24x}{4x^6}\right)^2 = \frac{36}{x^{10}}$

27) $\left(\frac{x^5}{x^7y^2}\right)^2 = \frac{1}{x^4y^4}$

28) $\left(\frac{xy^2}{x^2y^3}\right)^3 = \frac{1}{x^3y^3}$

29) $\left(\frac{4xy^4}{x^5}\right)^2 = \frac{16 \quad 8}{x^8}$

30) $\left(\frac{xy^4}{5xy^2}\right)^3 = \frac{y^6}{125}$

Homework: #.....

Zero and Negative Exponents

✍ *Evaluate the following expressions.*

1) $1^{-1} =$

2) $2^{-2} =$

3) $0^{15} =$

4) $1^{-10} =$

5) $8^{-1} =$

6) $8^{-2} =$

7) $2^{-4} =$

8) $10^{-2} =$

9) $9^{-2} =$

10) $3^{-3} =$

11) $7^{-3} =$

12) $3^{-4} =$

13) $6^{-3} =$

14) $5^{-3} =$

15) $22^{-1=}$

16) $4^{-4} =$

17) $5^{-4} =$

18) $15^{-2} =$

19) $4^{-5} =$

20) $9^{-3} =$

21) $3^{-5} =$

22) $5^{-4} =$

23) $12^{-3} =$

24) $15^{-3} =$

25) $20^{-3} =$

26) $50^{-2} =$

27) $18^{-3} =$

28) $24^{-2} =$

29) $30^{-3} =$

30) $10^{-5} =$

31) $\left(\frac{1}{8}\right)^{-1}$

32) $\left(\frac{1}{5}\right)^{-2} =$

33) $\left(\frac{1}{7}\right)^{-2} =$

34) $\left(\frac{2}{3}\right)^{-2} =$

35) $\left(\frac{1}{5}\right)^{-3} =$

36) $\left(\frac{3}{4}\right)^{-2} =$

37) $\left(\frac{2}{5}\right)^{-2} =$

38) $\left(\frac{1}{2}\right)^{-8} =$

39) $\left(\frac{2}{5}\right)^{-3} =$

40) $\left(\frac{3}{7}\right)^{-2} =$

41) $\left(\frac{5}{6}\right)^{-3} =$

42) $\left(\frac{4}{9}\right)^{-2} =$

Zero and Negative Exponents - Answers

✎Evaluate the following expressions.

1) $1^{-1} = 1$

2) $2^{-2} = \frac{1}{4}$

3) $0^{15} = 0$

4) $1^{-10} = 1$

5) $8^{-1} = \frac{1}{8}$

6) $8^{-2} = \frac{1}{64}$

7) $2^{-4} = \frac{1}{16}$

8) $10^{-2} = \frac{1}{100}$

9) $9^{-2} = \frac{1}{81}$

10) $3^{-3} = \frac{1}{27}$

11) $7^{-3} = \frac{1}{343}$

12) $3^{-4} = \frac{1}{81}$

13) $6^{-3} = \frac{1}{216}$

14) $5^{-3} = \frac{1}{125}$

15) $22^{-1} = \frac{1}{22}$

16) $4^{-4} = \frac{1}{256}$

17) $5^{-4} = \frac{1}{625}$

18) $15^{-2} = \frac{1}{225}$

19) $4^{-5} = \frac{1}{1,024}$

20) $9^{-3} = \frac{1}{729}$

21) $3^{-5} = \frac{1}{243}$

22) $5^{-4} = \frac{1}{625}$

23) $12^{-2} = \frac{1}{144}$

24) $15^{-3} = \frac{1}{3,375}$

25) $20^{-3} = \frac{1}{8,000}$

26) $50^{-2} = \frac{1}{2,500}$

27) $18^{-3} = \frac{1}{5,832}$

28) $24^{-2} = \frac{1}{576}$

29) $30^{-3} = \frac{1}{27,000}$

30) $10^{-5} = \frac{1}{100,000}$

31) $\left(\frac{1}{8}\right)^{-1} = 8$

32) $\left(\frac{1}{5}\right)^{-2} = 25$

33) $\left(\frac{1}{7}\right)^{-2} = 49$

34) $\left(\frac{2}{3}\right)^{-2} = \frac{9}{4}$

35) $\left(\frac{1}{5}\right)^{-3} = 125$

36) $\left(\frac{3}{4}\right)^{-2} = \frac{64}{27}$

37) $\left(\frac{2}{5}\right)^{-2} = \frac{25}{4}$

38) $\left(\frac{1}{2}\right)^{-8} = 256$

39) $\left(\frac{2}{5}\right)^{-3} = \frac{125}{8}$

40) $\left(\frac{3}{7}\right)^{-2} = \frac{49}{9}$

41) $\left(\frac{5}{6}\right)^{-3} = \frac{216}{125}$

42) $\left(\frac{4}{9}\right)^{-2} = \frac{81}{16}$

Negative Exponents and Negative Bases

✎ *Simplify and write the answer.*

1) $-3^{-1} =$

2) $-5^{-2} =$

3) $-2^{-4} =$

4) $-x^{-3} =$

5) $2x^{-1} =$

6) $-4x^{-3} =$

7) $-12x^{-5} =$

8) $-5x^{-2}y^{-3} =$

9) $20x^{-4}y^{-1} =$

10) $14a^{-6}b^{-7} =$

11) $-12x^2y^{-3} =$

12) $-\dfrac{25}{x^{-6}} =$

13) $-\dfrac{2x}{a^{-4}} =$

14) $\left(-\dfrac{1}{3x}\right)^{-2} =$

15) $\left(-\dfrac{3}{4x}\right)^{-2} =$

16) $-\dfrac{9}{a^{-7}b^{-2}} =$

17) $-\dfrac{5x}{x^{-3}} =$

18) $-\dfrac{a^{-3}}{b^{-2}} =$

19) $-\dfrac{8}{x^{-3}} =$

20) $\dfrac{5b}{-9c^{-4}} =$

21) $\dfrac{9ab}{a^{-3}b^{-1}} =$

22) $-\dfrac{15a^{-2}}{30b^{-3}} =$

23) $\dfrac{4ab^{-2}}{-3c^{-2}} =$

24) $\left(\dfrac{3a}{2c}\right)^{-2} =$

25) $\left(-\dfrac{5x}{3yz}\right)^{-3} =$

26) $\dfrac{11ab^{-2}}{-3c^{-2}} =$

27) $\left(-\dfrac{x^3}{x^4}\right)^{-2} =$

28) $\left(-\dfrac{x^{-2}}{3x^2}\right)^{-3} =$

Homework: #.....

Negative Exponents and Negative Bases - Answers

✎ *Simplify and write the answer.*

1) $-3^{-1} = -\frac{1}{3}$

2) $-5^{-2} = -\frac{1}{25}$

3) $-2^{-4} = -\frac{1}{16}$

4) $-x^{-3} = -\frac{1}{x^3}$

5) $2x^{-1} = \frac{2}{x}$

6) $-4x^{-3} = -\frac{4}{x^3}$

7) $-12x^{-5} = -\frac{12}{x^5}$

8) $-5x^{-2}y^{-3} = -\frac{5}{x^2y^3}$

9) $20x^{-4}y^{-1} = \frac{20}{x^4y}$

10) $14a^{-6}b^{-7} = \frac{14}{a^6b^7}$

11) $-12x^2y^{-3} = -\frac{12x^2}{y^3}$

12) $-\frac{25}{x^{-6}} = -25x^6$

13) $-\frac{2x}{a^{-4}} = -2xa^4$

14) $(-\frac{1}{3x})^{-2} = 9x^2$

15) $(-\frac{3}{4x})^{-2} = \frac{16x^2}{9}$

16) $-\frac{9}{a^{-7}b^{-2}} = -9a^7b^2$

17) $-\frac{5x}{x^{-3}} = -5x^4$

18) $-\frac{a^{-3}}{b^{-2}} = -\frac{b^2}{a^3}$

19) $-\frac{8}{x^{-3}} = -8x^3$

20) $\frac{5b}{-9c^{-4}} = -\frac{5bc^4}{9}$

21) $\frac{9ab}{a^{-3}b^{-1}} = 9a^4b^2$

22) $-\frac{15a^{-2}}{30b^{-3}} = -\frac{b^3}{2a^2}$

23) $\frac{4ab^{-2}}{-3c^{-2}} = -\frac{4ac^2}{3b^2}$

24) $(\frac{3a}{2c})^{-2} = \frac{4c^2}{9a^2}$

25) $(-\frac{5x}{3yz})^{-3} = -\frac{27y^3z^3}{125x^3}$

26) $\frac{11ab^{-2}}{-3c^{-2}} = -\frac{11ac^2}{3b^2}$

27) $(-\frac{x^3}{x^4})^{-2} = x^2$

28) $(-\frac{x^{-2}}{3x^2})^{-3} = -27x^{12}$

Scientific Notation

✎ *Write each number in scientific notation.*

1) 0.113 =

2) 0.02 =

3) 7.5 =

4) 20 =

5) 60 =

6) 0.004 =

7) 78 =

8) 1,600 =

9) 1,450 =

10) 31,000 =

11) 2,000,000 =

12) 0.0000003 =

13) 554,000 =

14) 0.000725 =

15) 0.00034 =

16) 86,000,000 =

17) 62,000 =

18) 97,000,000 =

19) 0.0000045 =

20) 0.0019 =

✎ *Write each number in standard notation.*

21) 2×10^{-1} =

22) 8×10^{-2} =

23) 1.8×10^{3} =

24) 9×10^{-4} =

25) 1.7×10^{-2} =

26) 9×10^{3} =

27) 7×10^{5} =

28) 1.15×10^{4} =

29) 7×10^{-5} =

30) 8.3×10^{-5} =

Scientific Notation - Answers

✎ *Write each number in scientific notation.*

1) $0.113 = 1.13 \times 10^{-1}$

2) $0.02 = 2 \times 10^{-2}$

3) $7.5 = 2.5 \times 10^{0}$

4) $20 = 2 \times 10^{1}$

5) $60 = 6 \times 10^{1}$

6) $0.004 = 4 \times 10^{-3}$

7) $78 = 7.8 \times 10^{1}$

8) $1{,}600 = 1.6 \times 10^{3}$

9) $1{,}450 = 1.45 \times 10^{3}$

10) $31{,}000 = 3.1 \times 10^{4}$

11) $2{,}000{,}000 = 2 \times 10^{6}$

12) $0.0000003 = 3 \times 10^{-7}$

13) $554{,}000 = 5.54 \times 10^{5}$

14) $0.000725 = 7.25 \times 10^{-4}$

15) $0.00034 = 3.4 \times 10^{-4}$

16) $86{,}000{,}000 = 8.6 \times 10^{7}$

17) $62{,}000 = 6.2 \times 10^{4}$

18) $97{,}000{,}000 = 9.7 \times 10^{7}$

19) $0.0000045 = 4.5 \times 10^{-6}$

20) $0.0019 = 1.9 \times 10^{-3}$

✎ *Write each number in standard notation.*

21) $2 \times 10^{-1} = 0.2$

22) $8 \times 10^{-2} = 0.08$

23) $1.8 \times 10^{3} = 1{,}800$

24) $9 \times 10^{-4} = 0.0009$

25) $1.7 \times 10^{-2} = 0.017$

26) $9 \times 10^{3} = 9{,}000$

27) $7 \times 10^{5} = 700{,}000$

28) $1.15 \times 10^{4} = 11{,}500$

29) $7 \times 10^{-5} = 0.00007$

30) $8.3 \times 10^{-5} = 0.000083$

Homework: #.....

Radicals

✎ *Simplify and write the answer.*

1) $\sqrt{0} = $ _____   9) $\sqrt{64} = $ _____   17) $\sqrt{324} = $ _____

2) $\sqrt{1} = $ _____   10) $\sqrt{81} = $ _____   18) $\sqrt{400} = $ _____

3) $\sqrt{4} = $ _____   11) $\sqrt{121} = $ _____   19) $\sqrt{900} = $ _____

4) $\sqrt{16} = $ _____   12) $\sqrt{225} = $ _____   20) $\sqrt{529} = $ _____

5) $\sqrt{9} = $ _____   13) $\sqrt{144} = $ _____   21) $\sqrt{361} = $ _____

6) $\sqrt{25} = $ _____   14) $\sqrt{100} = $ _____   22) $\sqrt{169} = $ _____

7) $\sqrt{49} = $ _____   15) $\sqrt{256} = $ _____   23) $\sqrt{196} = $ _____

8) $\sqrt{36} = $ _____   16) $\sqrt{289} = $ _____   24) $\sqrt{90} = $ _____

✎ *Evaluate.*

25) $\sqrt{6} \times \sqrt{6} = $ 31) $\sqrt{25} \times \sqrt{16} = $

26) $\sqrt{5} \times \sqrt{5} = $ 32) $\sqrt{25} \times \sqrt{64} = $

27) $\sqrt{8} \times \sqrt{8} = $ 33) $\sqrt{81} \times \sqrt{25} = $

28) $\sqrt{2} + \sqrt{2} = $ 34) $5\sqrt{3} \times 2\sqrt{3} = $

29) $\sqrt{8} + \sqrt{8} = $ 35) $8\sqrt{2} \times 2\sqrt{2} = $

30) $6\sqrt{5} - 2\sqrt{5} = $ 36) $6\sqrt{3} - \sqrt{12} = $

Homework: #.....

Radicals - Answers

✍ *Simplify and write the answer.*

1) $\sqrt{0} = 0$

2) $\sqrt{1} = 1$

3) $\sqrt{4} = 2$

4) $\sqrt{16} = 4$

5) $\sqrt{9} = 3$

6) $\sqrt{25} = 5$

7) $\sqrt{49} = 7$

8) $\sqrt{36} = 6$

9) $\sqrt{64} = 8$

10) $\sqrt{81} = 9$

11) $\sqrt{121} = 11$

12) $\sqrt{225} = 15$

13) $\sqrt{144} = 12$

14) $\sqrt{100} = 10$

15) $\sqrt{256} = 16$

16) $\sqrt{289} = 17$

17) $\sqrt{324} = 18$

18) $\sqrt{400} = 20$

19) $\sqrt{900} = 30$

20) $\sqrt{529} = 23$

21) $\sqrt{361} = 19$

22) $\sqrt{169} = 13$

23) $\sqrt{196} = 14$

24) $\sqrt{90} = 3\sqrt{10}$

✍ *Evaluate.*

25) $\sqrt{6} \times \sqrt{6} = 6$

26) $\sqrt{5} \times \sqrt{5} = 5$

27) $\sqrt{8} \times \sqrt{8} = 8$

28) $\sqrt{2} + \sqrt{2} = 2\sqrt{2}$

29) $\sqrt{8} + \sqrt{8} = 2\sqrt{8} = 4\sqrt{2}$

30) $6\sqrt{5} - 2\sqrt{5} = 4\sqrt{5}$

31) $\sqrt{25} \times \sqrt{16} = 20$

32) $\sqrt{25} \times \sqrt{64} = 40$

33) $\sqrt{81} \times \sqrt{25} = 45$

34) $5\sqrt{3} \times 2\sqrt{3} = 30$

35) $8\sqrt{2} \times 2\sqrt{2} = 32$

36) $6\sqrt{3} - \sqrt{12} = 4\sqrt{3}$

Simplifying Polynomials

✍ *Simplify each expression.*

1) $2(2x + 2) =$

_____

2) $4(4x - 2) =$

_____

3) $3(5x + 3) =$

_____

4) $6(7x + 5) =$

_____

5) $-3(8x - 7) =$

_____

6) $2x(3x + 4) =$

_____

7) $3x^2 + 3x^2 - 2x^3 =$

_____

8) $2x - x^2 + 6x^3 + 4 =$

_____

9) $5x + 2x^2 - 9x^3 =$

_____

10) $7x^2 + 5x^4 - 2x^3 =$

_____

11) $-3x^2 + 5x^3 + 6x^4 =$

_____

12) $(x - 3)(x - 4) =$

_____

13) $(x - 5)(x + 4) =$

_____

14) $(x - 6)(x - 3) =$

_____

15) $(2x + 5)(x + 8) =$

_____

16) $(3x - 8)(x + 4) =$

_____

17) $-8x^2 + 2x^3 - 10x^4 + 5x =$

_____

18) $11 - 6x^2 + 5x^2 - 12x^3 + 22 =$

_____

19) $2x^2 - 2x + 3x^3 + 12x - 22x =$

_____

20) $11 - 4x^2 + 3x^2 - 7x^3 + 3 =$

_____

21) $2x^5 - x^3 + 8x^2 - 2x^5 =$

_____

22) $(2x^3 - 1) + (3x^3 - 2x^3) =$

_____

Name:	Date: ....

Homework: #.....

Simplifying Polynomials - Answers

🖎 *Simplify each expression.*

1) $2(2x + 2) =$

$4x + 4$

2) $4(4x - 2) =$

$16x - 8$

3) $3(5x + 3) =$

$15x + 9$

4) $6(7x + 5) =$

$42x + 30$

5) $-3(8x - 7) =$

$-24x + 21$

6) $2x(3x + 4) =$

$6x^2 + 8x$

7) $3x^2 + 3x^2 - 2x^3 =$

$-2x^3 + 6x^2$

8) $2x - x^2 + 6x^3 + 4 =$

$6x^3 - x^2 + 2x + 4$

9) $5x + 2x^2 - 9x^3 =$

$-9x^3 + 2x^2 + 5x$

10) $7x^2 + 5x^4 - 2x^3 =$

$5x^4 - 2x^3 + 7x^2$

11) $-3x^2 + 5x^3 + 6x^4 =$

$6x^4 + 5x^3 - 3x^2$

12) $(x - 3)(x - 4) =$

$x^2 - 7x + 12$

13) $(x - 5)(x + 4) =$

$x^2 - x - 20$

14) $(x - 6)(x - 3) =$

$x^2 - 9x + 18$

15) $(2x + 5)(x + 8) =$

$2x^2 + 21x + 40$

16) $(3x - 8)(x + 4) =$

$3x^2 + 4x - 32$

17) $-8x^2 + 2x^3 - 10x^4 + 5x =$

$-10x^4 + 2x^3 - 8x^2 + 5x$

18) $11 - 6x^2 + 5x^2 - 12x^3 + 22 =$

$-12x^3 - x^2 + 33$

19) $2x^2 - 2x + 3x^3 + 12x - 22x =$

$3x^3 + 2x^2 - 12x$

20) $11 - 4x^2 + 3x^2 - 7x^3 + 3 =$

$-7x^3 - x^2 + 14$

21) $2x^5 - x^3 + 8x^2 - 2x^5 =$

$-x^3 + 8x^2$

22) $(2x^3 - 1) + (3x^3 - 2x^3) =$

$3x^3 - 1$

Homework: #.....

Adding and Subtracting Polynomials

✎ *Add or subtract expressions.*

1) $(x^2 - 3) + (x^2 + 1) =$

_____

2) $(2x^2 - 4) - (2 - 4x^2) =$

_____

3) $(x^3 + 2x^2) - (x^3 + 5) =$

_____

4) $(3x^3 - x^2) + (4x^2 - 7x) =$

_____

5) $(2x^3 + 3x) - (5x^3 + 2) =$

_____

6) $(5x^3 - 2) + (2x^3 + 10) =$

_____

7) $(7x^3 + 5) - (9 - 4x^3) =$

_____

8) $(5x^2 + 3x^3) - (2x^3 + 6) =$

_____

9) $(8x^2 - x) + (4x - 8x^2) =$

_____

10) $(6x + 9x^2) - (5x + 2) =$

_____

11) $(7x^4 - 2x) - (6x - 2x^4) =$

_____

12) $(2x - 4x^3) - (9x^3 + 6x) =$

_____

13) $(8x^3 - 8x^2) - (6x^2 - 3x) =$

_____

14) $(9x^2 - 6) + (5x^2 - 4x^3) =$

_____

15) $(8x^3 + 3x^4) - (x^4 - 3x^3) =$

_____

16) $(-4x^3 - 2x) + (5x - 2x^3) =$

_____

17) $(6x - 4x^4) - (8x^4 + 3x) =$

_____

18) $(7x - 8x^2) - (9x^4 - 3x^2) =$

_____

19) $(9x^3 - 6) + (9x^3 - 5x^2) =$

_____

20) $(5x^3 + x^4) - (8x^4 - 7x^3) =$

_____

Homework: #.....

Adding and Subtracting Polynomials - Answers

✎ *Add or subtract expressions.*

1) $(x^2 - 3) + (x^2 + 1) =$

$2x^2 - 2$

2) $(2x^2 - 4) - (2 - 4x^2) =$

$6x^2 - 6$

3) $(x^3 + 2x^2) - (x^3 + 5) =$

$2x^2 - 5$

4) $(3x^3 - x^2) + (4x^2 - 7x) =$

$3x^3 + 3x^2 - 7x$

5) $(2x^3 + 3x) - (5x^3 + 2) =$

$-3x^3 + 3x^2 - 2$

6) $(5x^3 - 2) + (2x^3 + 10) =$

$7x^3 + 8$

7) $(7x^3 + 5) - (9 - 4x^3) =$

$11x^3 - 4$

8) $(5x^2 + 3x^3) - (2x^3 + 6) =$

$x^3 + 5x^2 - 6$

9) $(8x^2 - x) + (4x - 8x^2) =$

$3x$

10) $(6x + 9x^2) - (5x + 2) =$

$9x^2 + x - 2$

11) $(7x^4 - 2x) - (6x - 2x^4) =$

$9x^4 - 8x$

12) $(2x - 4x^3) - (9x^3 + 6x) =$

$-13x^3 - 4x$

13) $(8x^3 - 8x^2) - (6x^2 - 3x) =$

$8x^3 - 14x^2 + 3x$

14) $(9x^2 - 6) + (5x^2 - 4x^3) =$

$-4x^3 + 14x^2 - 6$

15) $(8x^3 + 3x^4) - (x^4 - 3x^3) =$

$2x^4 + 11x^3$

16) $(-4x^3 - 2x) + (5x - 2x^3) =$

$-6x^3 + 3x$

17) $(6x - 4x^4) - (8x^4 + 3x) =$

$-12x^4 + 3x$

18) $(7x - 8x^2) - (9x^4 - 3x^2) =$

$-9x^4 - 5x^2 + 7x$

19) $(9x^3 - 6) + (9x^3 - 5x^2) =$

$18x^3 - 5x^2 - 6$

20) $(5x^3 + x^4) - (8x^4 - 7x^3) =$

$-7x^4 + 12x^3$

Multiplying Monomials

✎ *Simplify each expression.*

1) $5x^8 \times x^3 =$

2) $5y^5 \times 6y^3 =$

3) $-4z^7 \times 5z^5 =$

4) $7x^5y \times 3xy^2 =$

5) $-6xy^8 \times 3x^5y^3 =$

6) $7a^4b^2 \times 3a^8b =$

7) $5xy^5 \times 3x^3y^4 =$

8) $5p^5q^4 \times (-6pq^4) =$

9) $8s^6t^2 \times 6s^3t^7 =$

10) $(-8x^5y^2) \times 4x^6y^3 =$

11) $9xy^6z \times 3y^4z^2 =$

12) $12x^5y^4 \times 2x^8y =$

13) $4pq^5 \times (-7p^4q^8) =$

14) $9s^4t^2 \times (-5st^5) =$

15) $10p^3q^5 \times (-4p^4q^6) =$

16) $(-5p^2q^4r) \times 7pq^5r^3 =$

17) $(-9a^4b^7c^4) \times (-4a^7b) =$

18) $7u^5v^9 \times (-5u^{12}v^7) =$

19) $5u^3v^9z^2 \times (-4uv^9z) =$

20) $(-9xy^2z^4) \times 2x^2yz^5 =$

21) $8x^3y^2z^5 \times (-9x^4y^2z) =$

22) $6a^8b^8c^{12} \times 9a^7b^5c^8 =$

Multiplying Monomials - Answers

✎ *Simplify each expression.*

1) $5x^8 \times x^3 =$

$5x^{11}$

2) $5y^5 \times 6y^3 =$

$30y^8$

3) $-4z^7 \times 5z^5 =$

$-20z^{12}$

4) $7x^5y \times 3xy^2 =$

$21x^6y^3$

5) $-6xy^8 \times 3x^5y^3 =$

$-18x^6y^{11}$

6) $7a^4b^2 \times 3a^8b =$

$21a^{12}b^3$

7) $5xy^5 \times 3x^3y^4 =$

$15x^4y^9$

8) $5p^5q^4 \times (-6pq^4) =$

$-30p^6q^8$

9) $8s^6t^2 \times 6s^3t^7 =$

$42s^9t^9$

10) $(-8x^5y^2) \times 4x^6y^3 =$

$-32x^{11}y^5$

11) $9xy^6z \times 3y^4z^2 =$

$27xy^{10}z^3$

12) $12x^5y^4 \times 2x^8y =$

$24x^{13}y^5$

13) $4pq^5 \times (-7p^4q^8) =$

$-28p^5q^{13}$

14) $9s^4t^2 \times (-5st^5) =$

$-45s^5t^7$

15) $10p^3q^5 \times (-4p^4q^6) =$

$-40p^7q^{11}$

16) $(-5p^2q^4r) \times 7pq^5r^3 =$

$-35p^3q^9r^4$

17) $(-9a^4b^7c^4) \times (-4a^7b) =$

$36a^{11}b^8c^4$

18) $7u^5v^9 \times (-5u^{12}v^7) =$

$-35u^{17}v^{16}$

19) $5u^3v^9z^2 \times (-4uv^9z) =$

$-20u^4v^{18}z^3$

20) $(-9xy^2z^4) \times 2x^2yz^5 =$

$-18x^3y^3z^9$

21) $8x^3y^2z^5 \times (-9x^4y^2z) =$

$-72x^7y^4z^6$

22) $6a^8b^8c^{12} \times 9a^7b^5c^8 =$

$54a^{15}b^{13}c^{20}$

Homework: #.....

Multiplying and Dividing Monomials

✍ *Simplify each expression.*

1) $(8x^3)(2x^2) =$

_____

2) $(4x^6)(5x^4) =$

_____

3) $(-6x^8)(3x^3) =$

_____

4) $(5x^8y^9)(-6x^6y^9) =$

_____

5) $(8x^5y^6)(3x^2y^5) =$

_____

6) $(8yx^2)(7y^5x^3) =$

_____

7) $(4x^2y)(2x^2y^3) =$

_____

8) $(-2x^9y^4)(-9x^6y^8) =$

_____

9) $(-5x^8y^2)(-6x^4y^5) =$

_____

10) $(8x^8y)(-7x^4y^3) =$

_____

11) $(9x^6y^2)(6x^7y^4) =$

_____

12) $(8x^9y^5)(6x^5y^4) =$

_____

13) $(-5x^8y^9)(7x^7y^8) =$

_____

14) $(6x^2y^5)(5x^3y^2) =$

_____

15) $(9x^5y^{12})(4x^7y^9) =$

_____

16) $(-10x^{14}y^8)(2x^7y^5) =$

_____

17) $\dfrac{8x^4y^3}{xy^2} =$

_____

18) $\dfrac{6x^5y^6}{2x^3y} =$

_____

19) $\dfrac{12\ ^3y^7}{4x} =$

_____

20) $\dfrac{-20x^8y^9}{5x^5y^4} =$

_____

Homework: #.....

Multiplying and Dividing Monomials - Answers

✎ *Simplify each expression.*

1) $(8x^3)(2x^2) =$

$16x^5$

2) $(4x^6)(5x^4) =$

$20x^{10}$

3) $(-6x^8)(3x^3) =$

$-18x^{11}$

4) $(5x^8y^9)(-6x^6y^9) =$

$-30x^{14}y^{18}$

5) $(8x^5y^6)(3x^2y^5) =$

$24x^7y^{11}$

6) $(8yx^2)(7y^5x^3) =$

$56y^6x^5$

7) $(4x^2y)(2x^2y^3) =$

$8x^4y^4$

8) $(-2x^9y^4)(-9x^6y^8) =$

$18x^{15}y^{12}$

9) $(-5x^8y^2)(-6x^4y^5) =$

$30x^{12}y^7$

10) $(8x^8y)(-7x^4y^3) =$

$-56x^{12}y^4$

11) $(9x^6y^2)(6x^7y^4) =$

$54x^{13}y^6$

12) $(8x^9y^5)(6x^5y^4) =$

$48x^{14}y^9$

13) $(-5x^8y^9)(7x^7y^8) =$

$-35x^{15}y^{17}$

14) $(6x^2y^5)(5x^3y^2) =$

$30x^5y^7$

15) $(9x^5y^{12})(4x^7y^9) =$

$36x^{12}y^{21}$

16) $(-10x^{14}y^8)(2x^7y^5) =$

$-20x^{21}y^{13}$

17) $\dfrac{8x^4y^3}{xy^2} =$

$8x^3y$

18) $\dfrac{6x^5y^6}{2x^3y} =$

$3x^2y^5$

19) $\dfrac{12x^3y^7}{4xy} =$

$3x^2y^6$

20) $\dfrac{-20x^8y^9}{5x^5y^4} =$

$-4x^3y^5$

Multiplying a Polynomial and a Monomial

✎ *Find each product.*

1) $x(x - 2) =$

_____

2) $2(2 + x) =$

_____

3) $x(x - 1) =$

_____

4) $x(x + 3) =$

_____

5) $2x(x - 2) =$

_____

6) $5(4x + 3) =$

_____

7) $4x(3x - 4) =$

_____

8) $x(5x + 2y) =$

_____

9) $3x(x - 2y) =$

_____

10) $6x(3x - 4y) =$

_____

11) $2x(3x - 8) =$

_____

12) $6x(4x - 6y) =$

_____

13) $3x(4x - 2y) =$

_____

14) $2x(2x - 6y) =$

_____

15) $5x(x^2 + y^2) =$

_____

16) $3x(2x^2 - y^2) =$

_____

17) $7(2x^2 + 9y^2) =$

_____

18) $2x(-2x^2y + 3y) =$

_____

19) $-2(2x^2 - 4xy + 2) =$

_____

20) $5(x^2 - 6xy - 8) =$

_____

Multiplying a Polynomial and a Monomial - Answers

✎ *Find each product.*

1) $x(x-2) =$

$x^2 - 2x$

2) $2(2+x) =$

$2x + 4$

3) $x(x-1) =$

$x^2 - x$

4) $x(x+3) =$

$x^2 - 3x$

5) $2x(x-2) =$

$2x^2 - 4x$

6) $5(4x+3) =$

$20x + 15$

7) $4x(3x-4) =$

$12x^2 - 16x$

8) $x(5x+2y) =$

$5x^2 + 2xy$

9) $3x(x-2y) =$

$3x^2 - 6xy$

10) $6x(3x-4y) =$

$18x^2 - 24xy$

11) $2x(3x-8) =$

$6x^2 - 16x$

12) $6x(4x-6y) =$

$24x^2 - 36xy$

13) $3x(4x-2y) =$

$12x^2 - 6xy$

14) $2x(2x-6y) =$

$4x^2 - 12xy$

15) $5x(x^2+y^2) =$

$5x^3 - 5xy^2$

16) $3x(2x^2-y^2) =$

$6x^3 - 3xy^2$

17) $7(2x^2+9y^2) =$

$14x^3 + 63y^2$

18) $2x(-2x^2y+3y) =$

$-4x^3y + 6xy$

19) $-2(2x^2-4xy+2) =$

$-4x^2 + 8xy - 4$

20) $5(x^2-6xy-8) =$

$5x^2 - 30xy - 40$

Multiplying Binomials

✎ *Find each product.*

1) $(x - 2)(x + 5) =$

_____

2) $(x + 4)(x + 2) =$

_____

3) $(x - 2)(x - 4) =$

_____

4) $(x - 8)(x - 2) =$

_____

5) $(x - 7)(x - 5) =$

_____

6) $(x + 6)(x + 2) =$

_____

7) $(x - 9)(x + 3) =$

_____

8) $(x - 8)(x - 5) =$

_____

9) $(x + 3)(x + 7) =$

_____

10) $(x - 9)(x + 4) =$

_____

11) $(x + 6)(x + 6) =$

_____

12) $(x + 7)(x + 7) =$

_____

13) $(x - 8)(x + 7) =$

_____

14) $(x + 9)(x + 9) =$

_____

15) $(x - 8)(x - 8) =$

_____

16) $(2x - 9)(x + 5) =$

_____

17) $(2x - 3)(x + 4) =$

_____

18) $(2x + 4)(x + 2) =$

_____

19) $(2x + 2)(x + 3) =$

_____

20) $(2x - 4)(2x + 2) =$

_____

Multiplying Binomials - Answers

✎ *Find each product.*

1) $(x - 2)(x + 5) =$

$x^2 + 3x - 10$

2) $(x + 4)(x + 2) =$

$x^2 + 6x + 8$

3) $(x - 2)(x - 4) =$

$x^2 - 6x + 8$

4) $(x - 8)(x - 2) =$

$x^2 - 10x + 16$

5) $(x - 7)(x - 5) =$

$x^2 - 12x + 35$

6) $(x + 6)(x + 2) =$

$x^2 + 8x + 12$

7) $(x - 9)(x + 3) =$

$x^2 - 6x - 27$

8) $(x - 8)(x - 5) =$

$x^2 - 13x + 40$

9) $(x + 3)(x + 7) =$

$x^2 + 10x + 21$

10) $(x - 9)(x + 4) =$

$x^2 - 5x - 36$

11) $(x + 6)(x + 6) =$

$x^2 + 12x + 36$

12) $(x + 7)(x + 7) =$

$x^2 + 14x + 49$

13) $(x - 8)(x + 7) =$

$x^2 - x - 56$

14) $(x + 9)(x + 9) =$

$x^2 + 18x + 81$

15) $(x - 8)(x - 8) =$

$x^2 - 16x + 64$

16) $(2x - 9)(x + 5) =$

$x^2 - 4x - 45$

17) $(2x - 3)(x + 4) =$

$2x^2 + 5x - 12$

18) $(2x + 4)(x + 2) =$

$2x^2 + 8x + 8$

19) $(2x + 2)(x + 3) =$

$2x^2 + 8x + 6$

20) $(2x - 4)(2x + 2) =$

$4x^2 - 4x - 8$

Homework: #.....

Factoring Trinomials

✎ *Factor each trinomial.*

1) $x^2 + 3x - 10 =$

_____

2) $x^2 + 6x + 8 =$

_____

3) $x^2 - 6x + 8 =$

_____

4) $x^2 - 10x + 16 =$

_____

5) $x^2 - 13x + 40 =$

_____

6) $x^2 + 8x + 12 =$

_____

7) $x^2 - 6x - 27 =$

_____

8) $x^2 - 14x + 48 =$

_____

9) $x^2 + 15x + 56 =$

_____

10) $x^2 - 5x - 36 =$

_____

11) $x^2 + 12x + 36 =$

_____

12) $x^2 + 16x + 63 =$

_____

13) $x^2 + x - 72 =$

_____

14) $x^2 + 18x + 81 =$

_____

15) $x^2 - 16x + 64 =$

_____

16) $x^2 - 18x + 81 =$

_____

17) $2x^2 + 8x + 6 =$

_____

18) $2x^2 + 6x - 8 =$

_____

19) $2x^2 + 12x + 10 =$

_____

20) $4x^2 + 6x - 28 =$

_____

Factoring Trinomials - Answers

✍ *Factor each trinomial.*

1) $x^2 + 3x - 10 =$

$(x - 2)(x + 5)$

2) $x^2 + 6x + 8 =$

$(x + 4)(x + 2)$

3) $x^2 - 6x + 8 =$

$(x - 2)(x - 4)$

4) $x^2 - 10x + 16 =$

$(x - 8)(x - 2)$

5) $x^2 - 13x + 40 =$

$(x - 8)(x - 5)$

6) $x^2 + 8x + 12 =$

$(x + 6)(x + 2)$

7) $x^2 - 6x - 27 =$

$(x - 9)(x + 3)$

8) $x^2 - 14x + 48 =$

$(x - 8)(x - 6)$

9) $x^2 + 15x + 56 =$

$(x + 8)(x + 7)$

10) $x^2 - 5x - 36 =$

$(x - 9)(x + 4)$

11) $x^2 + 12x + 36 =$

$(x + 6)(x + 6)$

12) $x^2 + 16x + 63 =$

$(x + 7)(x + 9)$

13) $x^2 + x - 72 =$

$(x - 8)(x + 9)$

14) $x^2 + 18x + 81 =$

$(x + 9)(x + 9)$

15) $x^2 - 16x + 64 =$

$(x - 8)(x - 8)$

16) $x^2 - 18x + 81 =$

$(x - 9)(x - 9)$

17) $2x^2 + 8x + 6 =$

$(2x + 2)(x + 3)$

18) $2x^2 + 6x - 8 =$

$(2x - 2)(x + 4)$

19) $2x^2 + 12x + 10 =$

$(2x + 2)(x + 5)$

20) $4x^2 + 6x - 28 =$

$(2x - 4)(2x + 7)$

114

Homework: #.....

The Pythagorean Theorem

✍ *Do the following lengths form a right triangle?*

1) _____

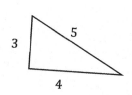

2) _____

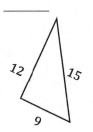

3) _____

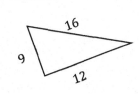

4) _____

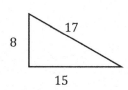

5) _____

6) _____

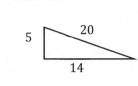

7) _____

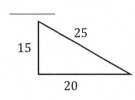

8) _____

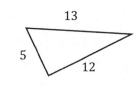

✍ *Find the missing side.*

9) _____

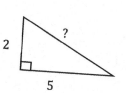

10) _____

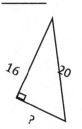

11) _____

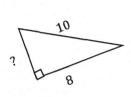

12) _____

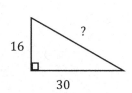

13) _____

14) _____

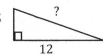

15) _____

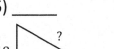

16) _____

Name:	Date: ....

Homework: #.....

The Pythagorean Theorem - Answers

✎ *Do the following lengths form a right triangle?*

1) yes

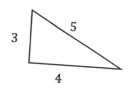

2) yes

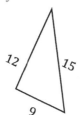

3) no

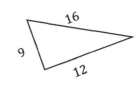

4) yes

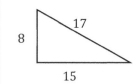

5) no

6) no

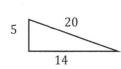

7) yes

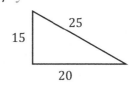

8) yes

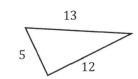

✎ *Find the missing side.*

9) 51

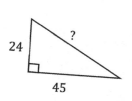

10) 12

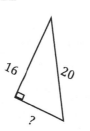

11) 6

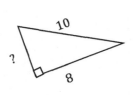

12) 34

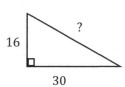

13) 26

14) 13

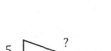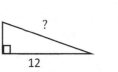

15) 30

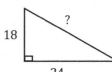

16) 52

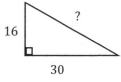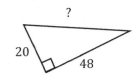

STAAR Grade 8 Math Workbook 2020 - 2021

Triangles

✍ *Find the measure of the unknown angle in each triangle.*

1) _____
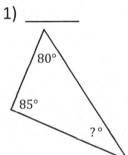

2) _____
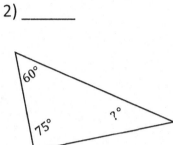

3) _____
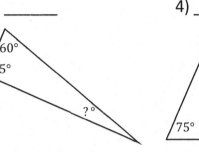

4) _____

5) _____
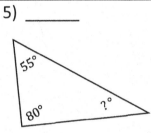

6) _____
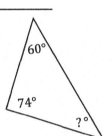

7) _____
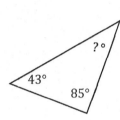

8) _____
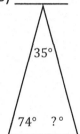

✍ *Find area of each triangle.*

9) _____
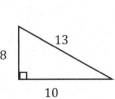

10) _____

11) _____
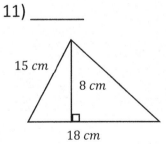

12) _____
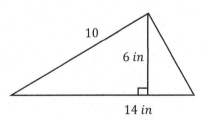

Triangles - Answers

 Find the measure of the unknown angle in each triangle.

1) 15°

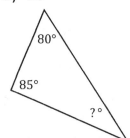
80°
85°
?°

2) 45°

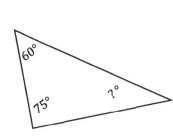
60°
75°
?°

3) 55°

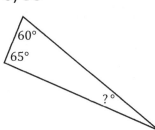
60°
65°
?°

4) 55°

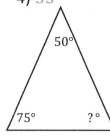
50°
75°
?°

5) 45°

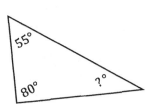
55°
80°
?°

6) 46°

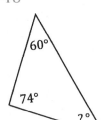
60°
74°
?°

7) 52°

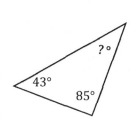
?°
43°
85°

8) 71°

35°
74°   ?°

 Find area of each triangle.

9) 40

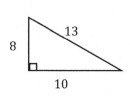
13
8
10

10) 56

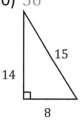
15
14
8

11) 72 cm^2

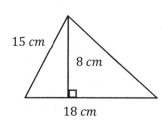
15 cm
8 cm
18 cm

12) 42 in^2

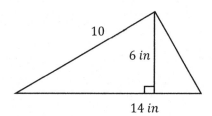
10
6 in
14 in

118

STAAR Grade 8 Math Workbook 2020 - 2021

Polygons

✎ *Find the perimeter of each shape.*

1) (square) _____

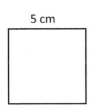

5 cm

2) _____

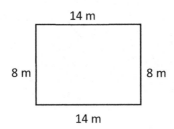

14 m
8 m   8 m
14 m

3) _____

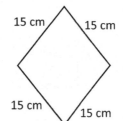

15 cm   15 cm
15 cm   15 cm

4) (square) _____

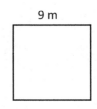

9 m

5) *(regular hexagon* _____

16 m

6) _____

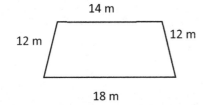

14 m
12 m   12 m
18 m

7) *(parallelogram* _____

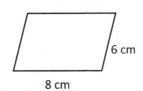

6 cm
8 cm

8) *(regular hexagon)* _____

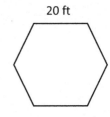

20 ft

9) _____

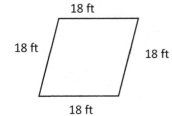

18 ft
18 ft   18 ft
18 ft

10) _____

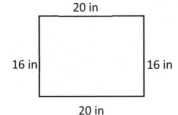

20 in
16 in   16 in
20 in

11) _____

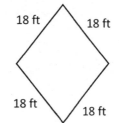

18 ft   18 ft
18 ft   18 ft

12) *(regular hexagon)* _____

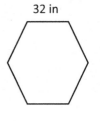

32 in

Polygons - Answers

✎ *Find the perimeter of each shape.*

1) (square) *20 cm*   2) *44 m*   3) *60 cm*   4) (square) *36 m*

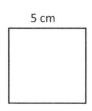

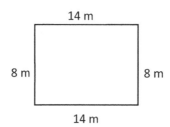

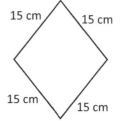

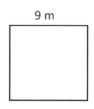

5) *(regular hexagon)*
96 m   6) *56 m*   7) *(parallelogram*
28 cm   8) *(regular*
hexagon) 120 ft

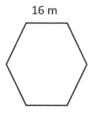

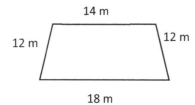

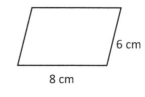

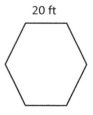

9) *72 ft*   10) *72 in*   11) *88 ft*   12) *(regular*
hexagon) 192 in

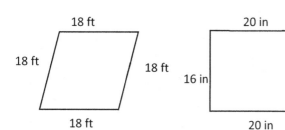

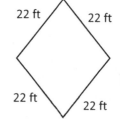

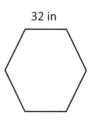

Homework: #.....

Circles

✎ *Find the Circumference of each circle.* (π = 3.14)

1) ____   2) ____   3) ____   4) ____   5) ____   6) ____

   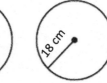   

7) ____   8) ____   9) ____   10) ____   11) ____   12) ____

✎ *Complete the table below.* (π = 3.14)

	Radius	Diameter	Circumference	Area
Circle 1	2 inches	4 inches	12.56 inches	12.56 square inches
Circle 2		8 meters		
Circle 3				113.04 square ft
Circle 4			50.24 miles	
Circle 5		9 km		
Circle 6	7 cm			
Circle 7		10 feet		
Circle 8				615.44 square meters
Circle 9			81.64 inches	
Circle 10	12 feet			

| Name: .... | Date: .... |

Homework: #.....

Circles - Answers

✎ *Find the Circumference of each circle.* (π = 3.14)

1) *43.96 in*   2) *75.36 cm*   3) *87.92 ft*   4) *81.64 m*   5) *113.04 cm*   6) *94.2 miles*

7) *119.32 in*   8) *138.16 ft*   9) *157 m*   10) *175.84 m*   11) *219.8 in*   12) *314 ft*

	Radius	Diameter	Circumference	Area
Circle 1	2 inches	4 inches	12.56 inches	12.56 square inches
Circle 2	4 meters	8 meters	25.12 meters	50.24 square meters
Circle 3	6 ft	12 ft	37.68	113.04 square ft
Circle 4	8 miles	16 miles	50.24 miles	200.96 square miles
Circle 5	4.5 km	9 km	28.26 km	63.585 square km
Circle 6	7 cm	14 cm	43.96 cm	153.86 square cm
Circle 7	5 feet	10 feet	31.4 feet	78.5 square feet
Circle 8	14 m	28 m	87.92 m	615.44 square meters
Circle 9	13 in	26 in	81.64 inches	530.66 square inches
Circle 10	12 feet	24 feet	75.36 feet	452.16 square feet

STAAR Grade 8 Math Workbook 2020 - 2021

Cubes

✎ *Find the volume of each cube.*

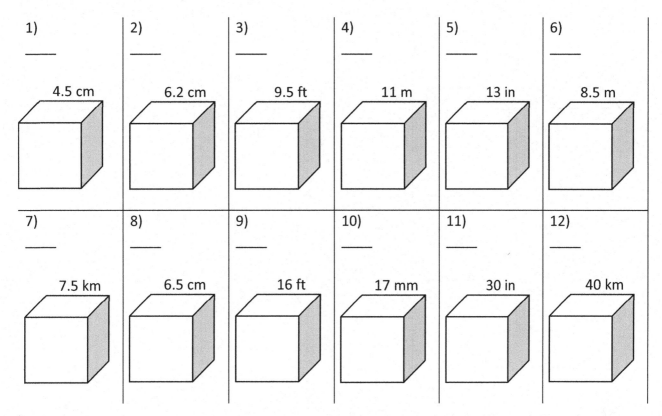

1) _____ 4.5 cm

2) _____ 6.2 cm

3) _____ 9.5 ft

4) _____ 11 m

5) _____ 13 in

6) _____ 8.5 m

7) _____ 7.5 km

8) _____ 6.5 cm

9) _____ 16 ft

10) _____ 17 mm

11) _____ 30 in

12) _____ 40 km

✎ *Find the surface area of each cube.*

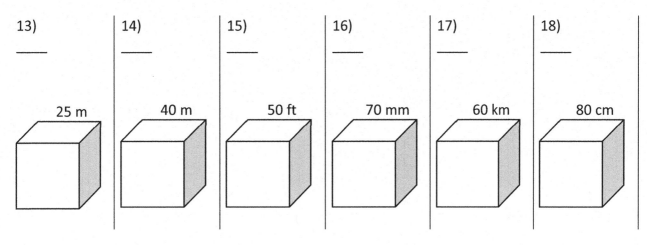

13) _____ 25 m

14) _____ 40 m

15) _____ 50 ft

16) _____ 70 mm

17) _____ 60 km

18) _____ 80 cm

Cubes - Answers

✎ *Find the volume of each cube.*

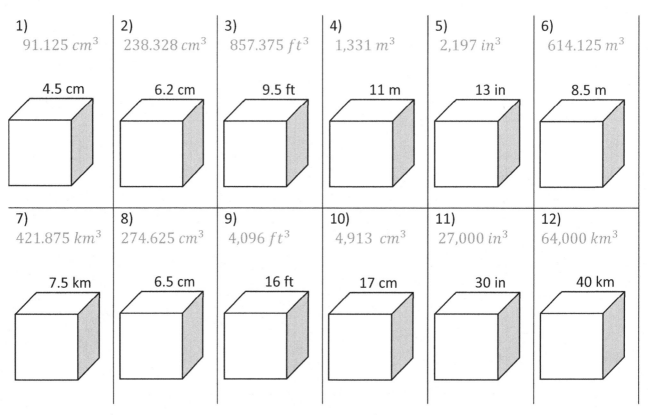

1) $91.125\ cm^3$	2) $238.328\ cm^3$	3) $857.375\ ft^3$	4) $1{,}331\ m^3$	5) $2{,}197\ in^3$	6) $614.125\ m^3$
4.5 cm	6.2 cm	9.5 ft	11 m	13 in	8.5 m
7) $421.875\ km^3$	8) $274.625\ cm^3$	9) $4{,}096\ ft^3$	10) $4{,}913\ cm^3$	11) $27{,}000\ in^3$	12) $64{,}000\ km^3$
7.5 km	6.5 cm	16 ft	17 cm	30 in	40 km

✎ *Find the surface area of each cube.*

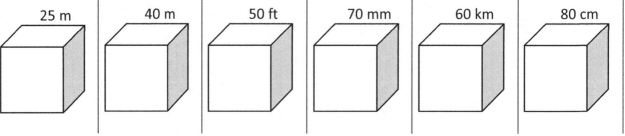

13) $3{,}750\ m^2$	14) $9{,}600\ m^2$	15) $15{,}000\ ft^2$	16) $29{,}400\ mm^2$	17) $21{,}600\ km^2$	18) $38{,}400\ cm^2$
25 m	40 m	50 ft	70 mm	60 km	80 cm

Homework: #.....

Trapezoids

✎ *Find the area of each trapezoid.*

1) _____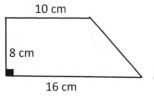

2) _____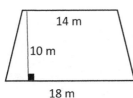

3) _____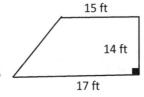

4) _____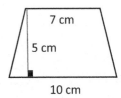

5) _____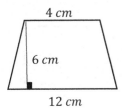

6) _____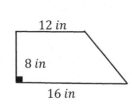

7) _____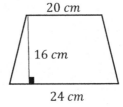

8) _____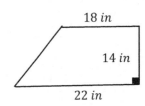

✎ *Solve.*

9) A trapezoid has an area of 80 cm^2 and its height is 8 cm and one base is 12 cm. What is the other base length? _____

10) If a trapezoid has an area of 120 ft^2 and the lengths of the bases are 14 ft and 16 ft, find the height. _____

11) If a trapezoid has an area of 160 m^2 and its height is 10 m and one base is 14 m, find the other base length. _____

12) The area of a trapezoid is 504 ft^2 and its height is 24 ft. If one base of the trapezoid is 14 ft, what is the other base length? _____

Name:	Date: ....

Homework: #.....

Trapezoids - Answers

 *Find the area of each trapezoid.*

1) $104\ cm^2$

2) $160\ m^2$

3) $224\ ft^2$

4) $324\ cm^2$

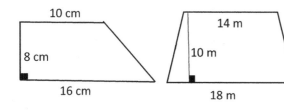

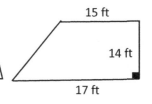

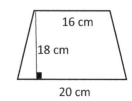

5) $288\ cm^2$

6) $414\ in^2$

7) $448\ cm^2$

8) $528\ in^2$

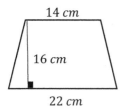

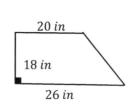

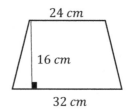

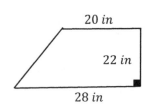

 *Solve.*

9) A trapezoid has an area of 80 cm² and its height is 8 cm and one base is 12 cm. What is the other base length? *8 cm*

10) If a trapezoid has an area of 120 ft² and the lengths of the bases are 14ft and 16ft, find the height. *8 ft*

11) If a trapezoid has an area of 160 m² and its height is 10 m and one base is 14 m, find the other base length. *18 m*

12) The area of a trapezoid is 504 ft² and its height is 24 ft. If one base of the trapezoid is 14 ft, what is the other base length? *28 ft*

Rectangular Prisms

✎ *Find the volume of each Rectangular Prism.*

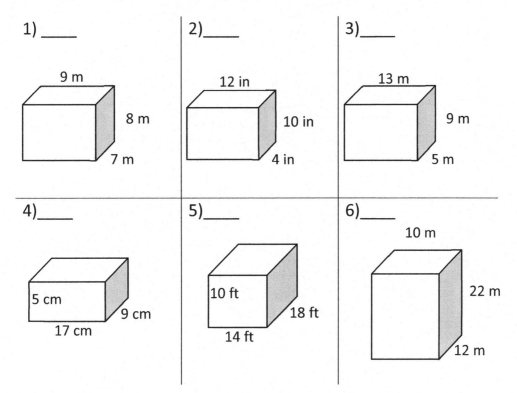

1) _____

9 m
8 m
7 m

2) _____

12 in
10 in
4 in

3) _____

13 m
9 m
5 m

4) _____

5 cm
9 cm
17 cm

5) _____

10 ft
18 ft
14 ft

6) _____

10 m
22 m
12 m

✎ *Find the surface area of each Rectangular Prism.*

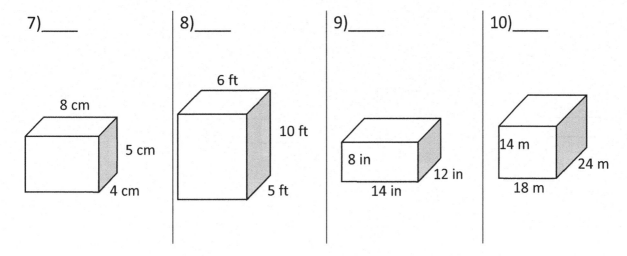

7) _____

8 cm
5 cm
4 cm

8) _____

6 ft
10 ft
5 ft

9) _____

8 in
12 in
14 in

10) _____

14 m
24 m
18 m

Rectangular Prisms - Answers

✍ *Find the volume of each Rectangular Prism.*

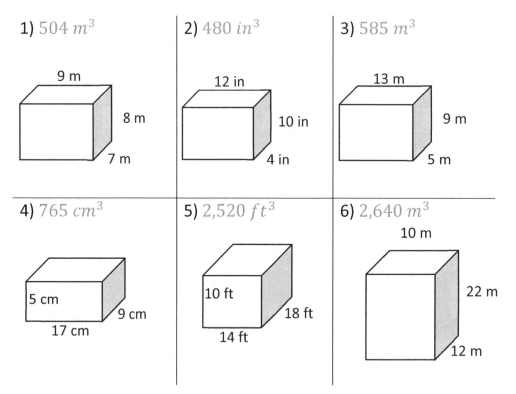

1) $504\ m^3$

9 m, 8 m, 7 m

2) $480\ in^3$

12 in, 10 in, 4 in

3) $585\ m^3$

13 m, 9 m, 5 m

4) $765\ cm^3$

5 cm, 9 cm, 17 cm

5) $2,520\ ft^3$

10 ft, 18 ft, 14 ft

6) $2,640\ m^3$

10 m, 22 m, 12 m

✍ *Find the surface area of each Rectangular Prism.*

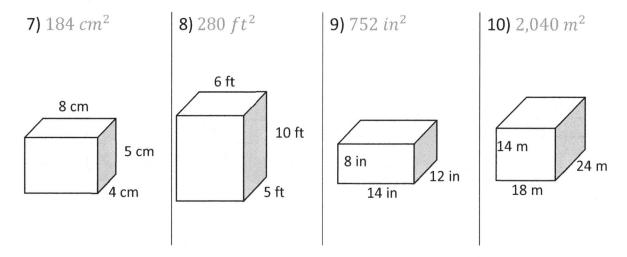

7) $184\ cm^2$

8 cm, 5 cm, 4 cm

8) $280\ ft^2$

6 ft, 10 ft, 5 ft

9) $752\ in^2$

8 in, 12 in, 14 in

10) $2,040\ m^2$

14 m, 24 m, 18 m

Name: ....   **Date:** ....

Homework: #.....

Cylinder

✎ *Find the volume of each Cylinder.* (π = 3.14)

1) _____
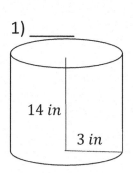

14 *in*

3 *in*

2) _____
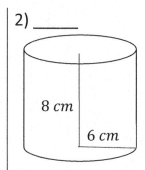

8 *cm*

6 *cm*

3) _____
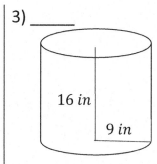

16 *in*

9 *in*

4) _____
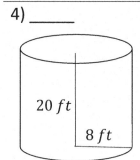

20 *ft*

8 *ft*

5) _____
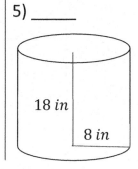

18 *in*

8 *in*

6) _____
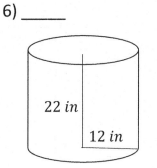

22 *in*

12 *in*

✎ *Find the surface area of each Cylinder.* (π = 3.14)

7) _____
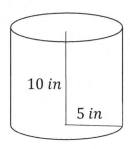

10 *in*

5 *in*

8) _____
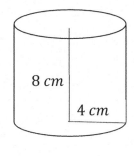

8 *cm*

4 *cm*

9) _____
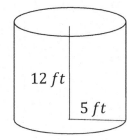

12 *ft*

5 *ft*

10) _____
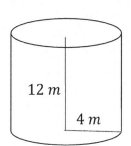

12 *m*

4 *m*

Homework: #.....

Cylinder - Answers

✎ *Find the volume of each Cylinder.* (π = 3.14)

1) $395.64 \ in^3$

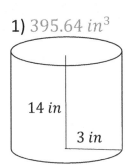

14 in

3 in

2) $904.32 \ cm^3$

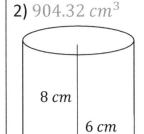

8 cm

6 cm

3) $4,069.44 \ in^3$

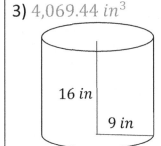

16 in

9 in

4) $4,019.2 \ ft^3$

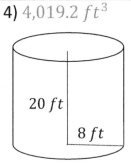

20 ft

8 ft

5) $3,617.28 \ in^3$

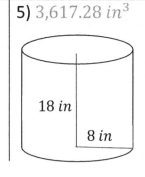

18 in

8 in

6) $9,947.52 \ in^3$

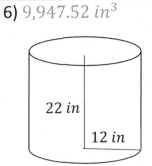

22 in

12 in

✎ *Find the surface area of each Cylinder.* (π = 3.14)

7) $471 \ in^2$

8) $301.44 \ cm^2$

9) $533.8 \ ft^2$

10) $401.92 \ m^2$

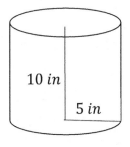

10 in

5 in

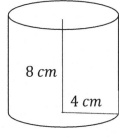

8 cm

4 cm

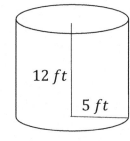

12 ft

5 ft

12 m

4 m

Homework: #.....

Mean, Median, Mode, and Range of the Given Data

✎ *Find the values of the Given Data.*

1) 6, 12, 1, 1, 5

Mode: _____   Range: _____

Mean: _____   Median: _____

2) 5, 8, 3, 7, 4, 3

Mode: _____   Range: _____

Mean: _____   Median: _____

3) 12, 5, 8, 7, 8

Mode: _____   Range: _____

Mean: _____   Median: _____

4) 8, 4, 10, 7, 3, 4

Mode: _____   Range: _____

Mean: _____   Median: _____

5) 9, 7, 10, 5, 7, 4, 14

Mode: _____   Range: _____

Mean: _____   Median: _____

6) 8, 1, 6, 6, 9, 2, 17

Mode: _____   Range: _____

Mean: _____   Median: _____

7) 12, 6, 1, 7, 9, 7, 8, 14

Mode: _____   Range: _____

Mean: _____   Median: _____

8) 10, 14, 5, 4, 11, 6, 13

Mode: _____   Range: _____

Mean: _____   Median: _____

9) 16, 15, 15, 16, 13, 14, 23

Mode: _____   Range: _____

Mean: _____   Median: _____

10) 16, 15, 12, 8, 4, 9, 8, 16

Mode: _____   Range: _____

Mean: _____   Median: _____

Mean, Median, Mode, and Range of the Given Data - Answers

✍ *Find the values of the Given Data.*

1) 6, 12, 1, 1, 5

Mode: 1   Range: 11

Mean: 5   Median: 5

2) 5, 8, 3, 7, 4, 3

Mode: 3   Range: 5

Mean: 5   Median: 4.5

3) 12, 5, 8, 7, 8

Mode: 8   Range: 7

Mean: 8   Median: 8

4) 8, 4, 10, 7, 3, 4

Mode: 4   Range: 7

Mean: 6   Median: 5.5

5) 9, 7, 10, 5, 7, 4, 14

Mode: 7   Range: 10

Mean: 8   Median: 7

6) 8, 1, 6, 6, 9, 2, 17

Mode: 6   Range: 16

Mean: 7   Median: 6

7) 12, 6, 1, 7, 9, 7, 8, 14

Mode: 7   Range: 13

Mean: 8   Median: 7.5

8) 10, 14, 5, 4, 11, 6, 13

Mode: *no mode* Range: 10

Mean: 9   Median: 10

9) 16, 15, 15, 16, 13, 14, 23

Mode: 15 *and* 16 Range: 10

Mean: 16   Median: 15

10) 16, 15, 12, 8, 4, 9, 8, 16

Mode: 8 *and* 16   Range: 12

Mean: 11   Median: 10.5

Homework: #.....

Pie Graph

✎ *The circle graph below shows all Wilson's expenses for last month. Wilson spent $200 on his bills last month.*

Answer following questions based on the Pie graph.

Wilson's last month expenses

Clothes 28%

Books 12%

Others 28%

Foods 22%

Bills 10%

1) How much was Wilson's total expenses last month? _____

2) How much did Wilson spend on his clothes last month? _____

3) How much did Wilson spend for foods last month? _____

4) How much did Wilson spend on his books last month? _____

5) What fraction is Wilson's expenses for his bills and clothes out of his total

   expenses last month? _____

Pie Graph - Answers

✎ *The circle graph below shows all Wilson's expenses for last month. Wilson spent $200 on his bills last month.*

Answer following questions based on the Pie graph.

Wilson's last month expenses

1) How much was Wilson's total expenses last month? $2,000

2) How much did Wilson spend on his clothes last month? $560

3) How much did Wilson spend for foods last month? $440

4) How much did Wilson spend on his books last month? $240

5) What fraction is Wilson's expenses for his bills and clothes out of his total expenses last month? $\frac{19}{50}$

Probability Problems

1) If there are 10 red balls and 20 blue balls in a basket, what is the probability that Oliver will pick out a red ball from the basket? _____

Gender	Under 45	45 or older	total
Male	12	6	18
Female	5	7	12
Total	17	13	30

2) The table above shows the distribution of age and gender for 30 employees in a company. If one employee is selected at random, what is the probability that the employee selected be either a female under age 45 or a male age 45 or older? _____

3) A number is chosen at random from 1 to 18. Find the probability of not selecting a composite number. (A composite number is a number that is divisible by itself, 1 and at least one other whole number) _____

4) There are 6 blue marbles, 8 red marbles, and 5 yellow marbles in a box. If Ava randomly selects a marble from the box, what is the probability of selecting a red or yellow marble? _____

5) A bag contains 19 balls: three green, five black, eight blue, a brown, a red and one white. If 18 balls are removed from the bag at random, what is the probability that a brown ball has been removed? _____

6) There are only red and blue marbles in a box. The probability of choosing a red marble in the box at random is one fourth. If there are 132 blue marbles, how many marbles are in the box? _____

Probability Problems - Answers

1) If there are 10 red balls and 20 blue balls in a basket, what is the probability that Oliver will pick out a red ball from the basket? $\frac{1}{3}$

Gender	Under 45	45 or older	total
Male	12	6	18
Female	5	7	12
Total	17	13	30

2) The table above shows the distribution of age and gender for 30 employees in a company. If one employee is selected at random, what is the probability that the employee selected be either a female under age 45 or a male age 45 or older? $\frac{11}{30}$

3) A number is chosen at random from 1 to 18. Find the probability of not selecting a composite number. (A composite number is a number that is divisible by itself, 1 and at least one other whole number) $\frac{7}{18}$

4) There are 6 blue marbles, 8 red marbles, and 5 yellow marbles in a box. If Ava randomly selects a marble from the box, what is the probability of selecting a red or yellow marble? $\frac{13}{19}$

5) A bag contains 19 balls: three green, five black, eight blue, a brown, a red and one white. If 18 balls are removed from the bag at random, what is the probability that a brown ball has been removed? $\frac{18}{19}$

6) There are only red and blue marbles in a box. The probability of choosing a red marble in the box at random is one fourth. If there are 132 blue marbles, how many marbles are in the box? 176

Homework: #.....

Permutations and Combinations

✎ *Calculate the value of each.*

1) $5! = $ ____

2) $6! = $ ____

3) $8! = $ ____

4) $5! + 6! = $ ____

5) $8! + 3! = $ ____

6) $6! + 7! = $ ____

7) $8! + 4! = $ ____

8) $9! - 3! = $ ____

✎ *Solve each word problems.*

9) Sophia is baking cookies. She uses milk, flour and eggs. How many different orders of ingredients can she try? _____

10) William is planning for his vacation. He wants to go to restaurant, watch a movie, go to the beach, and play basketball. How many different ways of ordering are there for him? _____

11) How many 7-digit numbers can be named using the digits 1, 2, 3, 4, 5, 6 and 7 without repetition? _____

12) In how many ways can 9 boys be arranged in a straight line? _____

13) In how many ways can 10 athletes be arranged in a straight line? _____

14) A professor is going to arrange her 7 students in a straight line. In how many ways can she do this? _____

15) How many code symbols can be formed with the letters for the word BLACK? _____

16) In how many ways a team of 7 basketball players can choose a captain and co-captain? _____

Permutations and Combinations - Answers

✎ *Calculate the value of each.*

1) $5! = 120$

2) $6! = 720$

3) $8! = 40,320$

4) $5! + 6! = 840$

5) $8! + 3! = 40,326$

6) $6! + 7! = 5,760$

7) $8! + 4! = 40,344$

8) $9! - 3! = 362,874$

✎ *Solve each word problems.*

9) Sophia is baking cookies. She uses milk, flour and eggs. How many different orders of ingredients can she try? 6

10) William is planning for his vacation. He wants to go to restaurant, watch a movie, go to the beach, and play basketball. How many different ways of ordering are there for him? 24

11) How many 7-digit numbers can be named using the digits 1, 2, 3, 4, 5, 6 and 7 without repetition? 5,040

12) In how many ways can 9 boys be arranged in a straight line? 362,880

13) In how many ways can 10 athletes be arranged in a straight line?

3,628,800

14) A professor is going to arrange her 7 students in a straight line. In how many ways can she do this? 5,040

15) How many code symbols can be formed with the letters for the word BLACK? 120

16) In how many ways a team of 7 basketball players can choose a captain and co-captain? 42

Function Notation and Evaluation

✎ *Evaluate each function.*

1) $f(x) = x - 1$, find $f(-1)$

_____

2) $g(x) = x + 3$, find $f(4)$

_____

3) $h(x) = x + 9$, find $f(3)$

_____

4) $f(x) = -x - 6$, find $f(5)$

_____

5) $f(x) = 2x - 7$, find $f(-1)$

_____

6) $w(x) = -2 - 4x$, find $w(5)$

_____

7) $g(n) = 6n - 3$, find $g(-2)$

_____

8) $h(x) = -8x + 12$, find $h(3)$

_____

9) $k(n) = 14 - 3n$, find $k(3)$

_____

10) $g(x) = 4x - 4$, find $g(-2)$

_____

11) $k(n) = 8n - 7$, find $k(4)$

_____

12) $w(n) = -2n + 14$, find $w(5)$

_____

13) $h(x) = 5x - 18$, find $h(8)$

_____

14) $g(n) = 2n^2 + 2$, find $g(5)$

_____

15) $f(x) = 3x^2 - 13$, find $f(2)$

_____

16) $g(n) = 5n^2 + 7$, find $g(-3)$

_____

17) $h(n) = 5n^2 - 10$, find $h(4)$

_____

18) $g(x) = -3x^2 - 6x$, find $g(2)$

_____

19) $k(n) = 3n^3 + 2n$, find $k(-5)$

_____

20) $f(x) = -4x + 12$, find $f(2x)$

_____

21) $k(a) = 6a + 5$, find $k(a - 1)$

_____

22) $h(x) = 9x + 3$, find $h(5x)$

_____

Function Notation and Evaluation

✒ *Evaluate each function.*

1) $f(x) = x - 1$, find $f(-1)$

-2

2) $g(x) = x + 3$, find $f(4)$

7

3) $h(x) = x + 9$, find $f(3)$

12

4) $f(x) = -x - 6$, find $f(5)$

-11

5) $f(x) = 2x - 7$, find $f(-1)$

-9

6) $w(x) = -2 - 4x$, find $w(5)$

-22

7) $g(n) = 6n - 3$, find $g(-2)$

-15

8) $h(x) = -8x + 12$, find $h(3)$

-12

9) $k(n) = 14 - 3n$, find $k(3)$

5

10) $g(x) = 4x - 4$, find $g(-2)$

-12

11) $k(n) = 8n - 7$, find $k(4)$

25

12) $w(n) = -2n + 14$, find $w(5)$

4

13) $h(x) = 5x - 18$, find $h(8)$

22

14) $g(n) = 2n^2 + 2$, find $g(5)$

52

15) $f(x) = 3x^2 - 13$, find $f(2)$

-1

16) $g(n) = 5n^2 + 7$, find $g(-3)$

52

17) $h(n) = 5n^2 - 10$, find $h(4)$

70

18) $g(x) = -3x^2 - 6x$, find $g(2)$

-24

19) $k(n) = 3n^3 + 2n$, find $k(-5)$

-385

20) $f(x) = -4x + 12$, find $f(2x)$

$-8x + 12$

21) $k(a) = 6a + 5$, find $k(a - 1)$

$6a - 1$

22) $h(x) = 9x + 3$, find $h(5x)$

$45x + 3$

Adding and Subtracting Functions

✍ *Perform the indicated operation.*

1) $f(x) = x + 6$

   $g(x) = 3x + 3$

   Find $(f - g)(2)$

   _____

2) $g(x) = x - 3$

   $f(x) = -x - 4$

   Find $(g - f)(-2)$

   _____

3) $h(t) = 5t + 4$

   $g(t) = 2t + 2$

   Find $(h + g)(-1)$

   _____

4) $g(a) = 3a - 5$

   $f(a) = a^2 + 6$

   Find $(g + f)(3)$

   _____

5) $g(x) = 4x - 5$

   $h(x) = 6x^2 + 5$

   Find $(g - f)(-2)$

   _____

6) $h(x) = x^2 + 3$

   $g(x) = -4x + 1$

   Find $(h + g)(4)$

   _____

7) $f(x) = -2x - 8$

   $g(x) = x^2 + 2$

   Find $(f - g)(6)$

   _____

8) $h(n) = -4n^2 + 9$

   $g(n) = 5n + 6$

   Find $(h - g)(5)$

   _____

9) $g(x) = 3x^2 - 2x - 1$

   $f(x) = 5x + 12$

   Find $(g - f)(a)$

   _____

10) $g(t) = -5t - 8$

    $f(t) = -t^2 + 2t + 12$

    Find $(g + f)(x)$

    _____

Homework: #.....

Adding and Subtracting Functions

✎ *Perform the indicated operation.*

1) $f(x) = x + 6$

   $g(x) = 3x + 3$

   Find $(f - g)(2)$

   -1

2) $g(x) = x - 3$

   $f(x) = -x - 4$

   Find $(g - f)(-2)$

   -3

3) $h(t) = 5t + 4$

   $g(t) = 2t + 2$

   Find $(h + g)(-1)$

   -1

4) $g(a) = 3a - 5$

   $f(a) = a^2 + 6$

   Find $(g + f)(3)$

   19

5) $g(x) = 4x - 5$

   $h(x) = 6x^2 + 5$

   Find $(g - f)(-2)$

   -42

6) $h(x) = x^2 + 3$

   $g(x) = -4x + 1$

   Find $(h + g)(4)$

   4

7) $f(x) = -2x - 8$

   $g(x) = x^2 + 2$

   Find $(f - g)(6)$

   -58

8) $h(n) = -4n^2 + 9$

   $g(n) = 5n + 6$

   Find $(h - g)(5)$

   -122

9) $g(x) = 3x^2 - 2x - 1$

   $f(x) = 5x + 12$

   Find $(g - f)(a)$

   $3a^2 - 7a - 13$

10) $g(t) = -5t - 8$

    $f(t) = -t^2 + 2t + 12$

    Find $(g + f)(x)$

    $-x^2 - 3x + 4$

Homework: #.....

Multiplying and Dividing Functions

✎ *Perform the indicated operation.*

1) $g(x) = x + 2$

   $f(x) = x + 3$

   Find $(g.f)(4)$

   _____

2) $f(x) = 2x$

   $h(x) = -x + 6$

   Find $(f.h)(-2)$

   _____

3) $g(a) = a + 2$

   $h(a) = 2a - 3$

   Find $(g.h)(5)$

   _____

4) $f(x) = 2x + 4$

   $h(x) = 4x - 2$

   Find $\left(\frac{f}{h}\right)(2)$

   _____

5) $f(x) = a^2 - 2$

   $g(x) = -4 + 3a$

   Find $\left(\frac{f}{g}\right)(2)$

   _____

6) $g(a) = 4a + 6$

   $f(a) = 2a - 8$

   Find $\left(\frac{g}{f}\right)(3)$

   _____

7) $g(t) = t^2 + 4$

   $h(t) = 2t - 4$

   Find $(g.h)(-3)$

   _____

8) $g(x) = x^2 + 2x + 5$

   $h(x) = 2x + 3$

   Find $(g.h)(2)$

   _____

9) $g(a) = 2a^2 - 4a + 2$

   $f(a) = 2a^3 - 2$

   Find $\left(\frac{g}{f}\right)(4)$

   _____

10) $g(x) = -4x^2 + 5 - 2x$

    $f(x) = x^2 - 2$

    Find $(g.f)(3)$

    _____

Multiplying and Dividing Functions

✎ *Perform the indicated operation.*

1) $g(x) = x + 2$

$f(x) = x + 3$

Find $(g \cdot f)(4)$

42

2) $f(x) = 2x$

$h(x) = -x + 6$

Find $(f \cdot h)(-2)$

-32

3) $g(a) = a + 2$

$h(a) = 2a - 3$

Find $(g \cdot h)(5)$

49

4) $f(x) = 2x + 4$

$h(x) = 4x - 2$

Find $\left(\dfrac{f}{h}\right)(2)$

$\dfrac{4}{3}$

5) $f(x) = a^2 - 2$

$g(x) = -4 + 3a$

Find $\left(\dfrac{f}{g}\right)(2)$

1

6) $g(a) = 4a + 6$

$f(a) = 2a - 8$

Find $\left(\dfrac{g}{f}\right)(3)$

-9

7) $g(t) = t^2 + 4$

$h(t) = 2t - 4$

Find $(g \cdot h)(-3)$

-130

8) $g(x) = x^2 + 2x + 5$

$h(x) = 2x + 3$

Find $(g \cdot h)(2)$

91

9) $g(a) = 2a^2 - 4a + 2$

$f(a) = 2a^3 - 2$

Find $\left(\dfrac{g}{f}\right)(4)$

$\dfrac{1}{7}$

10) $g(x) = -4x^2 + 5 - 2x$

$f(x) = x^2 - 2$

Find $(g \cdot f)(3)$

-259

Homework: #.....

Composition of Functions

🖎 **Using** $f(x) = x + 4$ **and** $g(x) = 2x$**, find:**

1) $f\big(g(1)\big) =$ ____

2) $f\big(g(-1)\big) =$ ____

3) $g\big(f(-2)\big) =$ ____

4) $g\big(f(2)\big) =$ ____

5) $f\big(g(2)\big) =$ ____

6) $g\big(f(3)\big) =$ ____

🖎 **Using** $f(x) = 2x + 5$ **and** $g(x) = x - 2$**, find:**

7) $g\big(f(2)\big) =$ ____

8) $g\big(f(-2)\big) =$ ____

9) $f\big(g(5)\big) =$ ____

10) $f\big(f(4)\big) =$ ____

11) $g\big(f(3)\big) =$ ____

12) $g\big(f(-3)\big) =$ ____

🖎 **Using** $f(x) = 4x - 2$ **and** $g(x) = x - 5$**, find:**

13) $g\big(f(-2)\big) =$ ____

14) $f\big(f(4)\big) =$ ____

15) $f\big(g(5)\big) =$ ____

16) $f\big(f(3)\big) =$ ____

17) $g\big(f(-3)\big) =$ ____

18) $g\big(g(6)\big) =$ ____

🖎 **Using** $f(x) = 5x + 3$ **and** $g(x) = 2x - 5$**, find:**

19) $f\big(g(-4)\big) =$ ____

20) $g\big(f(6)\big) =$ ____

21) $f\big(g(5)\big) =$ ____

22) $f\big(f(3)\big) =$ ____

| Name: .... | Date: .... |

Homework: #.....

Composition of Functions

✎ **Using** $f(x) = x + 4$ **and** $g(x) = 2x$, **find:**

1) $f\big(g(1)\big) = 6$

2) $f\big(g(-1)\big) = 2$

3) $g\big(f(-2)\big) = 4$

4) $g\big(f(2)\big) = 12$

5) $f\big(g(2)\big) = 8$

6) $g\big(f(3)\big) = 14$

✎ **Using** $f(x) = 2x + 5$ **and** $g(x) = x - 2$, **find:**

7) $g\big(f(2)\big) = 7$

8) $g\big(f(-2)\big) = -1$

9) $f\big(g(5)\big) = 11$

10) $f\big(f(4)\big) = 31$

11) $g\big(f(3)\big) = 9$

12) $g\big(f(-3)\big) = -3$

✎ **Using** $f(x) = 4x - 2$ **and** $g(x) = x - 5$, **find:**

13) $g\big(f(-2)\big) = -15$

14) $f\big(f(4)\big) = 54$

15) $f\big(g(5)\big) = -2$

16) $f\big(f(3)\big) = 38$

17) $g\big(f(-3)\big) = -19$

18) $g\big(g(6)\big) = -4$

✎ **Using** $f(x) = 5x + 3$ **and** $g(x) = 2x - 5$, **find:**

19) $f\big(g(-4)\big) = -62$

20) $g\big(f(6)\big) = 61$

21) $f\big(g(5)\big) = 28$

22) $f\big(f(3)\big) = 93$

146

STAAR Grade 8 Math Workbook 2020 - 2021

STAAR Test Review

The State of Texas Assessments of Academic Readiness (STAAR) is developed under the supervision of the Texas Education Agency and is taken by all public school students in Texas, grades 3–12. The tests measure the progress of students from 3rd grade to 8th grade, as well as high school. STAAR is the state's testing program and is based on state curriculum standards in core subjects including:

- o Reading,
- o Writing,
- o Mathematics,
- o Science,
- o Social Studies

In high school, students take end-of-course STAAR exams in five high school subjects:

- o Algebra I,
- o Biology,
- o English I,
- o English II,
- o U.S. History.

Students take STAAR tests in the spring. The number of tests a student takes each year will depend on what grade he or she is in. Most students will have two to four testing days during a school year.

In this book, there are two complete Grade 8 STAAR Math Tests. Take these tests to see what score you'll be able to receive on a real STAAR Math test.

Good luck!

Time to refine your skill with a practice examination

Take a practice STAAR Math Test to simulate the test day experience. After you've finished, score your test using the answer key.

Before You Start

- You'll need a pencil and a calculator to take the test.

- There are two types of questions:

  Multiple choice questions: for each of these questions, there are four or more possible answers. Choose which one is best.

  Grid-ins questions: for these questions, write your answer in the box provided.

- It's okay to guess. You won't lose any points if you're wrong.

- The STAAR Mathematics test contains a formula sheet, which displays formulas relating to geometric measurement and certain algebra concepts. Formulas are provided to test-takers so that they may focus on application, rather than the memorization, of formulas.

- After you've finished the test, review the answer key to see where you went wrong and what areas you need to improve.

Good luck!

STAAR Mathematics

Practice Test 1

2020-2021

Grade 8

Total number of questions: 40

Total time to complete the test: No time limit

You may use a calculator on this practice test.

STAAR Grade 8 Mathematics Formula Sheet

LINEAR EQUATIONS	
Slope – intercept form	$y = mx + b$
Direct Variation	$y = kx$
Slope of a Line	$m = \dfrac{y_2 - y_1}{x_2 - x_1}$

CIRCUMFERENCE	
Circle	$C = 2\pi r$ or $C = \pi d$

AREA	
Triangle	$A = \dfrac{1}{2}bh$
Parallelogram	$A = bh$
Trapezoid	$A = \dfrac{1}{2}h(b_1 + b_2)$
Circle	$A = \pi r^2$

SURFACE AREA		
	Lateral	Total
Prism	$S = Ph$	$S = Ph + 2B$
Cylinder	$S = 2\pi rh$	$S = 2\pi rh + 2\pi r^2$

VOLUME	
Prism or Cylinder	$V = Bh$
Pyramid or Cone	$V = \dfrac{1}{3}Bh$
Sphere	$V = \dfrac{4}{3}\pi r^3$

ADDITIONAL INFORMATION	
Pythagorean theorem	$a^2 + b^2 = c^2$
Simple interest	$I = prt$
Compound Interest	$A = p(1 + r)^t$

1) If x is directly proportional to the square of y, and $y = 2$ when $x = 12$, then when $x = 75$ $y = ?$

☐A. $\frac{1}{5}$ ☐B. 1

☐C. 5   ☐D. 12

2) Jack earns $616 for his first 44 hours of work in a week and is then paid 1.5 times his regular hourly rate for any additional hours. This week, Jack needs $826 to pay his rent, bills and other expenses. How many hours must he work to make enough money in this week?

☐A. 40   ☐B. 53

☐C. 48   ☐D. 54

Questions 3, 4 and 5 are based on the following data

Types of air pollutions in 10 cities of a country

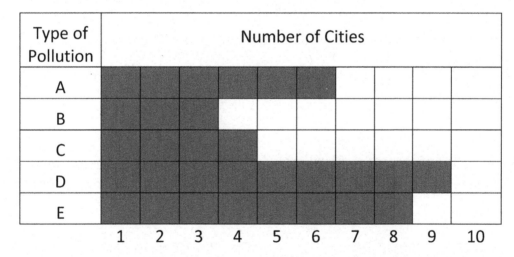

3) If a is the mean (average) of the number of cities in each pollution type category, b is the mode, and c is the median of the number of cities in each pollution type category, then which of the following must be true?

☐A. $a < b < c$ ☐B. $a = c$

☐C. $b < a < c$ ☐C. $b < c = a$

4) What percent of cities are in the type of pollution A, C, and E respectively?

☐A. 60%, 40%, 90%   ☐B. 30%, 40%, 90%

☐C. 30%, 40%, 60%   ☐D. 40%, 60%, 90%

5) How many cities should be added to type of pollutions B until the ratio of cities in type of pollution B to cities in type of pollution E will be 0.625?

☐A. 2   ☐B. 3

☐D. 4   ☐D. 5

6) In the following right triangle, if the sides AB and AC become twice longer, what will be the ratio of the perimeter of the triangle to its area?

☐A. $\frac{1}{2}$ ☐B. 2

☐C. $\frac{1}{3}$ ☐D. 3

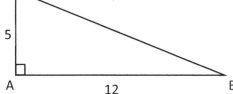

7) Which of the following is the same as: 0.000 000 000 000 042 121?

☐A. 4.2121×10^{14} ☐B. 4.2121×10^{-14}

☐C. $42,121 \times 10^{-10}$ ☐D. 42.121×10^{-13}

8) A shirt costing $200 is discounted 15%. After a month, the shirt is discounted another 15%. Which of the following expressions can be used to find the selling price of the shirt?

☐A. $(200)(0.70)$ ☐B. $(200) - 200(0.30)$

☐C. $(200)(0.15) - (200)(0.15)$ ☐D. $(200)(0.85)(0.85)$

9) Which of the following points lies on the line $2x + 4y = 10$

☐A. $(2, 1)$ ☐B. $(-1, 3)$

☐C. $(-2, 2)$ ☐D. $(2, 2)$

10) What is the value of the expression? $5 + 8 \times (-2) - [4 + 22 \times 5] \div 6$

Write your answer in the box below.

```
┌─────────────────────────┐
│                         │
└─────────────────────────┘
```

11) What is the area of the shaded region if the diameter of the bigger circle is 12 inches and the diameter of the smaller circle is 8 inches?

☐A. 16π ☐B. 20π

☐C. 36π ☐D. 80π

12) A student gets an 85% on a test with 40 questions. How many answers did the student solve correctly?

☐ A.25   ☐B. 28

☐ C.34   ☐D. 36

13) If 60% of A is 30% of B, then B is what percent of A?

☐A. 3%   ☐B. 30%

☐ C. 200%   ☐D. 300%

14) How many possible outfit combinations come from six shirts, three slacks, and five ties?

Write your answer in the box below.

```
┌─────────────────────────┐
│                         │
└─────────────────────────┘
```

15) A ladder leans against a wall forming a 60° angle between the ground and the ladder. If the bottom of the ladder is 30 feet away from the wall, how long is the ladder?

☐A.30 $feet$ ☐B. 40 $feet$

☐C. 50 $feet$ ☐D. 60 $feet$

16) When a number is subtracted from 24 and the difference is divided by that number, the result is 3. What is the value of the number?

☐A. 2   ☐B. 4

☐C. 6   ☐D. 12

17) An angle is equal to one fifth of its supplement. What is the measure of that angle in degrees?

☐A. 20°   ☐B. 30°

☐C. 45°   ☐D. 60°

18) John traveled $150\ km$ in 6 hours and Alice traveled $180\ km$ in 4 hours. What is the ratio of the average speed of John to average speed of Alice?

☐A. 3 : 2   ☐B. 2 : 3

☐C. 5 : 9   ☐D. 5 : 6

19) What is the value of y in the following system of equation?

$$3x - 4y = -40$$

$$-x + 2y = 10$$

Write your answer in the box below.

☐

20) In five successive hours, a car travels $40\ km, 45\ km, 50\ km, 35\ km$ and $55\ km$. In the next five hours, it travels with an average speed of $50\ km\ per\ hour$. Find the total distance the car traveled in 10 hours.

☐A. $425\ km$ ☐B. $450\ km$

☐C. $475\ km$ ☐D. $500\ km$

21) How long does a 420–miles trip take moving at 50 miles per hour (mph)?

    ☐A. 4 *hours*   ☐B. 6 *hours and* 24 *minutes*

    ☐C. 8 *hours and* 24 *minutes*   ☐D. 8 *hours and* 30 *minutes*

22) Right triangle ABC has two legs of lengths 6 cm (AB) and 8 cm (AC). What is the length of the third side (BC)?

    ☐ A. 4 cm ☐ B. 6 cm

    ☐ C. 8 cm ☐ D. 10 cm

23) The ratio of boys to girls in a school is $2:3$. If there are 600 students in a school, how many boys are in the school.

    Write your answer in the box below.

24) The perimeter of the trapezoid below is 54. What is its area?

    Write your answer in the box below.

25) Two third of 18 is equal to $\frac{2}{5}$ of what number?

    ☐A. 12   ☐B. 20

    ☐C. 30   ☐D. 60

26) The marked price of a computer is D dollar. Its price decreased by 20% in January and later increased by 10% in February. What is the final price of the computer in D dollar?

    ☐A. 0.80D ☐B. 0.88D

    ☐C. 0.90D ☐D. 1.20D

27) In 1999, the average worker's income increased $2,000 per year starting from $24,000 annual salary. Which equation represents income greater than average? (I = income, x = number of years after 1999)

□A. $I > 2{,}000\,x + 24{,}000$ □B. $I > -2{,}000\,x + 24{,}000$

□C. $I < -2000\,x + 24{,}000$ □D. $I < 2{,}000\,x - 24{,}000$

28) From last year, the price of gasoline has increased from $1.25 per gallon to $1.75 per gallon. The new price is what percent of the original price?

□A. 72% □B. 120%

□C. 140% □D. 160%

29) A boat sails 40 miles south and then 30 miles east. How far is the boat from its start point?

□A. 45 $miles$ □B. 50 $miles$

□C. 60 $miles$ □D. 70 $miles$

30) Jason purchased a laptop for $529.72. The laptop is regularly priced at $646.00. What was the percent discount Jason received on the laptop?

□A. 12% □B. 18%

□C. 20% □D. 25%

31) A bag contains 18 balls: two green, five black, eight blue, a brown, a red and one white. If 17 balls are removed from the bag at random, what is the probability that a brown ball has been removed?

□A. $\frac{1}{9}$ □B. $\frac{1}{6}$

□C. $\frac{16}{17}$ □D. $\frac{17}{18}$

32) The average of five consecutive numbers is 38. What is the smallest number?

□A. 38 □B. 36

□C. 34 □D. 12

33) A rope weighs 600 grams per meter of length. What is the weight in kilograms of 12.2 meters of this rope? (1 $kilograms$ = 1,000 $grams$)

☐A. 0.0732   ☐B. 0.732

☐C. 7.32   ☐D. 7.320

34) A chemical solution contains 4% alcohol. If there is 32 ml of alcohol, what is the volume of the solution?

☐A. 240 ml ☐B. 480 ml

☐C. 800 ml ☐D. 1200 ml

35) The average weight of 23 girls in a class is 60 kg and the average weight of 32 boys in the same class is 62 kg. What is the average weight of all the 55 students in that class?

☐A. 60   ☐B. 61.16

☐C. 61.68   ☐D. 62.90

36) The price of a laptop is decreased by 20% to $360. What is its original price?

☐A. 320   ☐B. 380

☐C. 400   ☐D. 450

37) The radius of the following cylinder is 6 inches and its height is 12 inches. What is the surface area of the cylinder in square inches?

Write your answer in the box below. (π equals 3.14)

38) The average of 13, 15, 20 and x is 15. What is the value of x?

Write your answer in the box below.

39) In the xy-plane, the point $(1, 2)$ and $(-1, 6)$ are on line A. Which of the following points could also be on line A?

☐A. $(-1, 2)$ ☐B. $(3, 4)$

☐C. $(5, 7)$ ☐D. $(3, -2)$

40) A bank is offering 4.5% simple interest on a savings account. If you deposit $9,000, how much interest will you earn in five years?

☐A. $405   ☐B. $720

☐C. $2,025   ☐D. $3,600

End of STAAR Mathematics Practice Test 1.

STAAR Mathematics

Practice Test 2

2020-2021

Grade 8

Total number of questions: 40

Total time to complete the test: No time limit

You may use a calculator on this practice test.

STAAR Grade 8 Mathematics Formula Sheet

LINEAR EQUATIONS	
Slope – intercept form	$y = mx + b$
Direct Variation	$y = kx$
Slope of a Line	$m = \dfrac{y_2 - y_1}{x_2 - x_1}$

CIRCUMFERENCE	
Circle	$C = 2\pi r$ or $C = \pi d$

AREA	
Triangle	$A = \dfrac{1}{2}bh$
Parallelogram	$A = bh$
Trapezoid	$A = \dfrac{1}{2}h(b_1 + b_2)$
Circle	$A = \pi r^2$

SURFACE AREA

	Lateral	Total
Prism	$S = Ph$	$S = Ph + 2B$
Cylinder	$S = 2\pi rh$	$S = 2\pi rh + 2\pi r^2$

VOLUME	
Prism or Cylinder	$V = Bh$
Pyramid or Cone	$V = \dfrac{1}{3}Bh$
Sphere	$V = \dfrac{4}{3}\pi r^3$

ADDITIONAL INFORMATION	
Pythagorean theorem	$a^2 + b^2 = c^2$
Simple interest	$I = prt$
Compound Interest	$A = p(1 + r)^t$

1) The capacity of a red box is 20% bigger than the capacity of a blue box. If the red box can hold 30 equal sized books, how many of the same books can the blue box hold?

☐A. 9   ☐B. 15

☐C. 21   ☐D. 25

2) The sum of six different negative integers is -70. If the smallest of these integers is -15, what is the largest possible value of one of the other five integers?

☐A. -14 ☐B. -10

☐C. -5 ☐D. -1

3) $[6 \times (-24) + 8] - (-4) + [4 \times 5] \div 2 = ?$

Write your answer in the box below.

4) Which of the following is equal to the expression below?

$$(2x + 2y)(2x - y)$$

☐A. $4x^2 - 2y^2$ ☐B. $2x^2 + 6xy - 2y^2$

☐C. $4x^2 - 2xy - 2y^2$ ☐D. $4x^2 + 2xy - 2y^2$

5) What is the product of all possible values of x in the following equation?

$$|x - 10| = 3$$

☐A. 3   ☐B. 7

☐C. 13   ☐D. 91

6) What is the slope of a line that is perpendicular to the line $4x - 2y = 12$?

☐A. -2 ☐B. $-\dfrac{1}{2}$

☐C. 4   ☐D. 12

7) What is the value of the expression $5(x + 2y) + (2 - x)^2$ when $x = 3$ and $y = -2$?

  ☐A. −4   ☐B. 20

  ☐C. 36   ☐D. 50

8) Bob is 12 miles ahead of Mike running at 6.5 miles per hour and Mike is running at the speed of 8 miles per hour. How long does it take Bob to catch Mike?

  ☐A. 3 *hours*   ☐B. 4 *hours*

  ☐C. 6 *hours*   ☐D. 8 *hours*

9) 44 students took an exam and 11 of them failed. What percent of the students passed the exam?

  ☐A. 20%   ☐B. 40%

  ☐C. 60%   ☐D. 75%

10) Which of the following graphs represents the compound inequality $-1 \leq 2x - 3 < 1$?

  ☐A.

  ☐B.

  ☐C.

  ☐D.
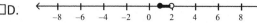

11) The diagonal of a rectangle is 13 inches long and the height of the rectangle is 5 inches. What is the area of the rectangle in inches?

  Write your answer in the box below.

  ┌─────────────────────┐
  │   │
  └─────────────────────┘

12) The perimeter of the trapezoid below is 40 cm. What is its area?

☐A. 576 cm^2 ☐B. 98 cm^2

☐C. 40 cm^2 ☐D. 24cm^2

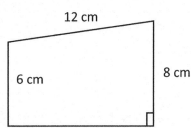

13) A card is drawn at random from a standard 52–card deck, what is the probability that the card is of Clubs? (The deck includes 13 of each suit clubs, diamonds, hearts, and spades)

☐A. $\dfrac{1}{3}$ ☐B. $\dfrac{1}{4}$

☐C. $\dfrac{1}{6}$ ☐D. $\dfrac{1}{52}$

14) The mean of 50 test scores was calculated as 80. But, it turned out that one of the scores was misread as 94 but it was 69. What is the mean?

☐A. 78.5   ☐B. 79.5

☐C. 80.5   ☐D. 88.5

15) Two dice are thrown simultaneously, what is the probability of getting a sum of 6 or 9?

☐A. $\dfrac{1}{3}$ ☐B. $\dfrac{1}{4}$

☐C. $\dfrac{1}{6}$ ☐D. $\dfrac{1}{12}$

16) A swimming pool holds 2,500 cubic feet of water. The swimming pool is 25 feet long and 10 feet wide. How deep is the swimming pool?
Write your answer in the box below. (<u>Don't write the measurement</u>)

17) Alice is choosing a menu for her lunch. She has 3 choices of appetizers, 5 choices of entrees, 6 choices of cake. How many different menu combinations are possible for her to choose?

☐A. 12   ☐B. 32

☐C. 90   ☐D. 120

18) Four one – foot rulers can be split among how many users to leave each with $\frac{1}{3}$ of a ruler?

☐A. 4   ☐B. 6

☐C. 12   ☐D. 24

19) What is the area of a square whose diagonal is 4?

☐A. 8   ☐B. 32

☐C. 36   ☐D. 64

20) Anita's trick–or–treat bag contains 15 pieces of chocolate, 10 suckers, 10 pieces of gum, 25 pieces of licorice. If she randomly pulls a piece of candy from her bag, what is the probability of her pulling out a piece of sucker?

☐A. $\frac{1}{3}$ ☐B. $\frac{1}{4}$

☐C. $\frac{1}{6}$ ☐D. $\frac{1}{12}$

21) The volume of a cube is less than $64\ m^3$. Which of the following can be the cube's side?
☐A. $2\ m$ ☐B. $5\ m$

☐C. $4\ m$ ☐D. $6\ m$

22) The perimeter of a rectangular yard is 72 meters. What is its length if its width is twice its length?

☐A. 12 meters   ☐B. 18 meters

☐C. 20 meters   ☐D. 24 meters

23) The average of 6 numbers is 10. The average of 4 of those numbers is 7. What is the average of the other two numbers.

☐A. 10   ☐B. 12

☐C. 14   ☐D. 16

24) What is the value of x in the following system of equations?

$$2x + 5y = 11$$
$$4x - 2y = -26$$

☐A. -1 ☐B. 1

☐C. -4.5 ☐D. 4.5

25) The area of a circle is less than $81\pi\ ft^2$. Which of the following can be the diameter of the circle?

☐A. $28ft$ ☐B. $18ft$

☐C. $20ft$ ☐D. $17ft$

26) The ratio of boys and girls in a class is $4:7$. If there are 55 students in the class, how many more boys should be enrolled to make the ratio $1:1$?

☐A. 8   ☐B. 10

☐C. 12   ☐D. 15

27) A football team had $20,000 to spend on supplies. The team spent $10,000 on new balls. New sport shoes cost $120 each. Which of the following inequalities represent the number of new shoes the team can purchase.

☐A. $120x + 10,000 \leq 20,000$ ☐B. $120x + 10,000 \geq 20,000$

☐C. $10,000x + 120 \leq 20,000$ ☐D. $10,000x + 12,0 \geq 20,000$

28) Jason needs an 70% average in his writing class to pass. On his first 4 exams, he earned scores of 68%, 72%, 85%, and 90%. What is the minimum score Jason can earn on his fifth and final test to pass?

Write your answer in the box below.

29) What is the value of x in the following equation? $\frac{2}{3}x + \frac{1}{6} = \frac{1}{2}$

☐A. 6   ☐B. $\frac{1}{2}$

☐C. $\frac{1}{3}$ ☐D. $\frac{1}{4}$

30) A bank is offering 3.5% simple interest on a savings account. If you deposit $14,000, how much interest will you earn in two years?

☐A. $490   ☐B. $980

☐C. $4,200   ☐D. $4,900

31) Simplify $5x^2y^3(2x^2y)^3 =$

☐A. $12x^4y^6$ ☐B. $12x^8y^6$

☐C. $40x^4y^6$ ☐D. $40x^8y^6$

32) What is the surface area of the cylinder below?

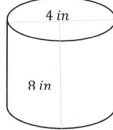

4 in

8 in

☐A. $28\,\pi\;in^2$ ☐B. $37\,\pi\;in^2$

☐C. $40\,\pi\;in^2$ ☐D. $288\,\pi\;in^2$

33) The average of four numbers is 48. If a fifth number that is greater than 65 is added, then, which of the following could be the new average?

☐A. 48   ☐B. 51

☐C. 50   ☐D. 52

34) A cruise line ship left Port A and traveled 50 miles due west and then 120 miles due north. At this point, what is the shortest distance from the cruise to port A in miles?

Write your answer in the box below.

35) What is the equivalent temperature of $140°F$ in Celsius? $C = \frac{5}{9}(F - 32)$

☐A. 32   ☐B. 40

☐C. 48   ☐D. 60

36) If 150% of a number is 75, then what is the 80% of that number?

☐A. 40   ☐B. 50

☐C. 70   ☐D.85

37) Simplify the expression. $(5x^3 - 8x^2 + 2x^4) - (4x^2 - 2x^4 + 2x^3)$

☐A. $4x^4 + 3x^3 - 12x^2$ ☐B. $4x^3 - 12x^2$

☐C. $4x^4 - 3x^3 - 12x^2$ ☐D. $8x^3 - 12x^2$

38) In two successive years, the population of a town is increased by 10% and 20%. What percent of the population is increased after two years?

☐A. 30%   ☐B. 32%

☐C. 34%   ☐D. 68%

39) Last week 25,000 fans attended a football match. This week three times as many bought tickets, but one sixth of them cancelled their tickets. How many are attending this week?

☐A. 48,000   ☐B. 54,000

☐C. 62,500   ☐D. 72,000

40) Which graph shows a non-proportional linear relationship between x and y?

☐ A.

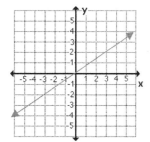

☐ B.

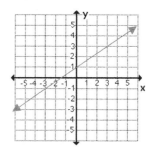

☐ C.

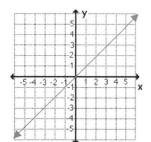

☐ D.

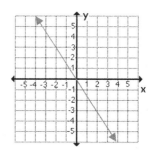

End of STAAR Mathematics Practice Test 2.

STAAR Mathematics Practice Tests

Answer Keys

Now, it's time to review your results to see where you went wrong and what areas you need to improve.

STAAR Math Practice Test 1				STAAR Math Practice Test 2			
1	C	21	C	1	D	21	A
2	D	22	D	2	C	22	A
3	C	23	240	3	−122	23	D
4	A	24	130	4	D	24	C
5	A	25	C	5	D	25	D
6	A	26	B	6	B	26	D
7	B	27	A	7	A	27	A
8	D	28	C	8	D	28	35
9	B	29	B	9	D	29	B
10	−30	30	B	10	D	30	B
11	B	31	D	11	60	31	D
12	C	32	B	12	B	32	C
13	C	33	C	13	B	33	D
14	90	34	C	14	B	34	130
15	D	35	B	15	B	35	D
16	C	36	D	16	10	36	A
17	B	37	678.24	17	C	37	A
18	C	38	12	18	C	38	B
19	−5	39	D	19	A	39	C
20	C	40	C	20	C	40	B

How to score your test

The basic score on each STAAR test is the raw score, which is simply the number of questions correct. On the STAAR test each subject test should be passed individually. It means that you must meet the standard on each section of the test. If you failed one subject test but did well enough on another, that's still not a passing score.

There are four possible scores that you can receive on the STAAR Math Grade 8 Test:

Do Not Meet: This indicates that your score is lower than the passing score. If you do not pass, you can reschedule to retake any the STAAR Math test. Students have three opportunities to retake test(s) and receive remedial help if they don't pass.

Approaches: This score indicates that your score meets the standard of t

Met the Standard: This indicates that your score meets Texas state standards for that subject.

Commended Performance: This indicates that you've mastered the skills that would be taught in your grade.

There are approximately 40 questions on STAAR Mathematics for grade 8. Similar to other subject areas, you will need a minimum score to pass the Mathematics Test. There are approximately 40 raw score points on the STAAR math test. The raw points correspond with correct answers. This will then be converted into your scaled score. Approximately, you need to get 28 out of 40 raw score to pass the STAAR Mathematics for grade 8.

To score your STAAR Mathematics practice tests, first find your raw score. There were 40 questions on each STAAR Mathematics practice test in this book. All questions have one point. Use the following table to convert your raw score to the scale score.

Raw Score	Scale Score	Result	Percentile
0	1065		0
1	1197		0
2	1276		0
3	1324		0
4	1359		0
5	1387		0
6	1411		0
7	1432		1
8	1451		2
9	1468		3
10	1484	Do Not Meet	4
11	1499		6
12	1513		8
13	1526		10
14	1539		12
15	1552		14
16	1564		16
17	1576		19
18	1588		22
19	1595		25
20	1611		27
21	1622		30
22	1634		34
23	1645	Approaches	37
24	1657		41
25	1669		44
26	1681		48
27	1693		52
28	1700		55
29	1719		60
30	1733		64
31	1747		68
32	1762	Meets	72
33	1779		76
34	1796		79
35	1815		83
36	1836		87
37	1854		89
38	1889	Masters	93
39	1925		96
40 or more	1973-2185		98-100

STAAR Mathematics Practice Tests

Answers and Explanations

STAAR Mathematics Practice Test 1

Answers and Explanations

1) Choice C is correct

x is directly proportional to the square of y. Then: $x = cy^2 \rightarrow 12 = c(2)^2 \rightarrow 12 = 4c \rightarrow c = \frac{12}{4} = 3$. The relationship between x and y is: $x = 3y^2$, $x = 75$

$$75 = 3y^2 \rightarrow y^2 = \frac{75}{3} = 25 \rightarrow y = 5$$

2) Choice D is correct

The amount of money that jack earns for one hour: $\frac{\$616}{44} = \$14$

Number of additional hours that he work to make enough money is: $\frac{\$826 - \$616}{1.5 \times \$14} = 10$

Number of total hours is: $44 + 10 = 54$

3) Choice B is correct

Let's find the mean (average), mode and median of the number of cities for each type of pollution. Number of cities for each type of pollution: 6, 3, 4, 9, 8

$$average\ (mean) = \frac{sum\ of\ terms}{number\ of\ terms} = \frac{6+3+4+9+8}{5} = \frac{30}{5} = 6$$

Median is the number in the middle. To find median, first list numbers in order from smallest to largest. 3, 4, 6, 8, 9. Median of the data is 6. Mode is the number which appears most often in a set of numbers. Therefore, there is no mode in the set of numbers. Median = Mean, then,

$a = c$

4) Choice A is correct

Percent of cities in the type of pollution A: $\frac{6}{10} \times 100 = 60\%$

Percent of cities in the type of pollution C: $\frac{4}{10} \times 100 = 40\%$

Percent of cities in the type of pollution E: $\frac{9}{10} \times 100 = 90\%$

5) Choice A is correct

Let the number of cities should be added to type of pollutions B be x. Then:

$$\frac{x+3}{8} = 0.625 \rightarrow x + 3 = 8 \times 0.625 \rightarrow x + 3 = 5 \rightarrow x = 2$$

6) Choice A is correct

$AB = 12$ And $AC = 5$. $BC = \sqrt{12^2 + 5^2} = \sqrt{144 + 25} = \sqrt{169} = 13$

Perimeter $= 5 + 12 + 13 = 30$.   Area $= \frac{5 \times 12}{2} = 5 \times 6 = 30$

In this case, the ratio of the perimeter of the triangle to its area is: $\frac{30}{30} = 1$

If the sides AB and AC become twice longer, then: $AB = 24$ And $AC = 10$

$BC = \sqrt{24^2 + 10^2} = \sqrt{576 + 100} = \sqrt{676} = 26$. Perimeter $= 26 + 24 + 10 = 60$

Area $= \frac{10 \times 24}{2} = 10 \times 12 = 120$

In this case the ratio of the perimeter of the triangle to its area is: $\frac{60}{120} = \frac{1}{2}$

7) Choice B is correct

In scientific notation all numbers are written in the form of: $m \times 10^n$, where m is between 1 and 10. To find an equivalent value of 0.000 000 000 000 042 121, move the decimal point to the right so that you have a number that is between 1 and 10. Then: 4.2121
Now, determine how many places the decimal moved in step 1, then put it as the power of 10. We moved the decimal point 14 places. Then: $10^{-14} \rightarrow$ When the decimal moved to the right, the exponent is negative. Then: $0.000\ 000\ 000\ 000\ 042\ 121 = 4.2121 \times 10^{-14}$

8) Choice D is correct

To find the discount, multiply the number by $(100\% - rate\ of\ discount)$.

Therefore, for the first discount we get: $(200)(100\% - 15\%) = (200)(0.85) = 170$

For the next 15% discount: $(200)(0.85)(0.85)$

9) Choice B is correct

Plug in each pair of number in the equation:

    A. $(2, 1)$: $2(2) + 4(1) = 8$
    B. $(-1, 3)$: $2(-1) + 4(3) = 10$
    C. $(-2, 2)$: $2(-2) + 4(2) = 4$
    D. $(2, 2)$: $2(2) + 4(2) = 12$

Only choice B is correct.

10) The answer is: -30

Use PEMDAS (order of operation): $5 + 8 \times (-2) - [4 + 22 \times 5] \div 6 = 5 + 8 \times (-2) - [4 + 110] \div 6 = 5 + 8 \times (-2) - [114] \div 6 = 5 + (-16) - 19 = 5 + (-16) - 19 = -11 - 19 = -30$

11) Choice B is correct.

To find the area of the shaded region subtract smaller circle from bigger circle.

$S_{bigger} - S_{smaller} = \pi (r_{bigger})^2 - \pi (r_{smaller})^2 \Rightarrow S_{bigger} - S_{smaller} = \pi (6)^2 - \pi (4)^2$

$\Rightarrow 36\pi - 16\pi = 20\pi$

12) Choice C is correct

85% of 40 is: $85\% \; of \; 40 = 0.85 \times 40 = 34$. So, the student solves 34 questions correctly.

13) Choice C is correct

Write the equation and solve for B: $0.60 \, A = 0.30 \, B$, divide both sides by 0.30, then:

$\frac{0.60}{0.30} A = B$, therefore: $B = 2 \, A$, and B is 2 times of A or it's 200% of A.

14) The answer is 90.

To find the number of possible outfit combinations, multiply number of options for each factor:

$6 \times 3 \times 5 = 90$

15) Choice D is correct

The relationship among all sides of special right triangle

$30° - 60° - 90°$ is provided in this triangle:

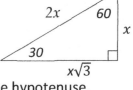
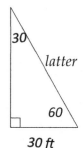

In this triangle, the opposite side of 30° angle is half of the hypotenuse.

Draw the shape for this question:

The latter is the hypotenuse. Therefore, the latter is $60 \, ft$.

16) Choice C is correct

Let x be the number. Write the equation and solve for x. $(24 - x) \div x = 3$. Multiply both sides by x. $(24 - x) = 3x$, then add x both sides. $24 = 4x$, now divide both sides by 4. $x = 6$

17) Choice B is correct

The sum of supplement angles is 180. Let x be that angle. Therefore, $x + 5x = 180$. $6 = 180$, divide both sides by 6: $x = 30$

18) Choice C is correct

The average speed of john is: $150 \div 6 = 25 \ km$, The average speed of Alice is: $180 \div 4 = 45 \ km$. Write the ratio and simplify. $25 : 45 \Rightarrow 5 : 9$

19) The answer is -5.

Solving Systems of Equations by Elimination

$$3x - 4y = -40$$
$$-x + 2y = 10$$ Multiply the second equation by 3, then add it to the first equation.

$$\frac{3x - 4y = -40}{3(-x + 2y = 10)} \Rightarrow \frac{3x - 4y = -40}{-3x + 6y = 30)} \Rightarrow 2y = -10 \Rightarrow y = -5$$

20) Choice C is correct

Add the first 5 numbers. $40 + 45 + 50 + 35 + 55 = 225$. To find the distance traveled in the next 5 hours, multiply the average by number of hours. $Distance = Average \times Rate = 50 \times 5 = 250$.   Add both numbers. $250 + 225 = 475$

21) Choice C is correct

Use distance formula: $Distance = Rate \times time \Rightarrow 420 = 50 \times T$, divide both sides by 50. $420 \div 50 = T \Rightarrow T = 8.4 \ hours$.

Change hours to minutes for the decimal part. $0.4 \ hours = 0.4 \times 60 = 24 \ minutes$.

22) Choice D is correct

Use Pythagorean Theorem: $a^2 + b^2 = c^2, 6^2 + 8^2 = c^2 \Rightarrow 100 = c^2 \Rightarrow c = 10$

23) The answer is 240.

Th ratio of boy to girls is $2 : 3$. Therefore, there are 2 boys out of 5 students. To find the answer, first divide the total number of students by 5, then multiply the result by 2.

$600 \div 5 = 120 \Rightarrow 120 \times 2 = 240$

24) The answer is 130.

The perimeter of the trapezoid is 54.

Therefore, the missing side (height) is $= 54 - 18 - 12 - 14 = 10$

Area of a trapezoid: $A = \frac{1}{2} h (b_1 + b_2) = \frac{1}{2}(10)(12 + 14) = 130$

25) Choice C is correct

Let x be the number. Write the equation and solve for x.

$\frac{2}{3} \times 18 = \frac{2}{5} . x \Rightarrow \frac{2 \times 18}{3} = \frac{2x}{5}$, use cross multiplication to solve for x.

$5 \times 36 = 2x \times 3 \Rightarrow 180 = 6x \Rightarrow x = 30$

26) Choice B is correct

To find the discount, multiply the number by $(100\% - rate\ of\ discount)$.

Therefore, for the first discount we get: $(D)(100\% - 20\%) = (D)(0.80) = 0.80\ D$

For increase of 10%: $(0.80\ D)(100\% + 10\%) = (0.80D)(1.10) = 0.88\ D = 88\%\ of\ D$

27) Choice A is correct

Let x be the number of years. Therefore, $2,000 per year equals $2000x$. starting from $24,000 annual salary means you should add that amount to $2000x$. Income more than that is:

$I > 2000x + 24000$

28) Choice C is correct

The question is this: 1.75 is what percent of 1.25? Use percent formula:

$$\text{part} = \frac{\text{percent}}{100} \times \text{whole} \Rightarrow 1.75 = \frac{percent}{100} \times 1.25 \Rightarrow 1.75 = \frac{percent \times 1.25}{100} \Rightarrow$$

$$175 = percent \times 1.25 \Rightarrow percent = \frac{175}{1.25} = 140$$

29) Choice B is correct

Use the information provided in the question to draw the shape.

Use Pythagorean Theorem: $a^2 + b^2 = c^2$

$40^2 + 30^2 = c^2 \Rightarrow 1600 + 900 = c^2 \Rightarrow 2500 = c^2 \Rightarrow c = 50$

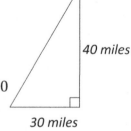

40 miles

30 miles

30) Choice B is correct

The question is this: 529.72 is what percent of 646? Use percent formula:

$$part = \frac{percent}{100} \times whole. \qquad 529.72 = \frac{percent}{100} \times 646 \Rightarrow 529.72 = \frac{percent \times 646}{100} \Rightarrow$$

$$529.72 = percent \times 646 \Rightarrow percent = \frac{529.72}{646} = 82$$

529.72 is 82% of 646. Therefore, the discount is: $100\% - 82\% = 18\%$

31) Choice D is correct

If 17 balls are removed from the bag at random, there will be one ball in the bag. The probability of choosing a brown ball is 1 out of 18. Therefore, the probability of not choosing a brown ball is 17 out of 18 and the probability of having not a brown ball after removing 17 balls is the same.

32) Choice B is correct

Let x be the smallest number. Then, these are the numbers: $x, x + 1, x + 2, x + 3, x + 4$

$$\text{average} = \frac{\text{sum of terms}}{\text{number of terms}} \Rightarrow 38 = \frac{x+(x+1)+(x+2)+(x+3)+(x+4)}{5} \Rightarrow 38 = \frac{5x+1}{5} \Rightarrow$$

$$190 = 5x + 10 \Rightarrow 180 = 5x \Rightarrow x = 36$$

33) Choice C is correct

The weight of 12.2 meters of this rope is: $12.2 \times 600 \, g = 7320 \, g$

$1 \, kg = 1000 \, g$, therefore, $7320 \, g \div 1000 = 7.32 \, kg$

34) Choice C is correct

4% of the volume of the solution is alcohol. Let x be the volume of the solution.

Then: $4\% \; of \; x = 32 \, ml \Rightarrow 0.04 \, x = 32 \Rightarrow x = 32 \div 0.04 = 800$

35) Choice B is correct

$\text{average} = \frac{\text{sum of terms}}{\text{number of terms}}$. The sum of the weight of all girls is: $23 \times 60 = 1,380 \, kg$, The sum of the weight of all boys is: $32 \times 62 = 1984 \, kg$. The sum of the weight of all students is: $1,380 + 1,984 = 3,364 \, kg$. $average = \frac{3364}{55} = 61.16$

36) Choice D is correct

Let x be the original price. If the price of a laptop is decreased by 20% to $360, then:

$80\% \; of \; x = 360 \Rightarrow 0.80x = 360 \Rightarrow x = 360 \div 0.80 = 450$

37) The answer is 678.24.

Surface Area of a cylinder $= 2\pi r(r + h)$, The radius of the cylinder is 6 inches and its height is 12 inches. π is about 3.14. Then: Surface Area of a cylinder $= 2(\pi)(6)(6 + 12) = 216 \, \pi = 678.24$

38) The answer is 12.

$$average = \frac{sum \; of \; terms}{number \; of \; terms} \Rightarrow 15 = \frac{13 + 15 + 20 + x}{4} \Rightarrow 60 = 48 + x \Rightarrow x = 12$$

39) Choice D is correct

The equation of a line is in the form of $y = mx + b$, where m is the slope of the line and b is the $y - intercept$ of the line. Two points $(1, 2)$ and $(-1, 6)$ are on line A. Therefore, the slope of the line A is: $slope \; of \; line \; A = \frac{y_2 - y_1}{x_2 - x_1} = \frac{6-2}{-1-1} = \frac{4}{-2} = -2$

The slope of line A is -2. Thus, the formula of the line A is: $y = mx + b = -2x + b$, choose a point and plug in the values of x and y in the equation to solve for b. Let's choose point $(1, 2)$. Then: $y = -2x + b \rightarrow 2 = -2(1) + b \rightarrow b = 2 + 2 = 4$. The equation of line A is: $y = -2x + 4$

Now, let's review the choices provided:

A. $(-1, 2)$ $y = -2x + 4 \rightarrow 2 = -2(-1) + 4 = 6$ This is not true.

B. $(5, 7)$ $y = -2x + 4 \rightarrow 7 = -2(5) + 4 = -6$ This is not true.

C. $(3, 4)$ $y = -2x + 4 \rightarrow 4 = -2(3) + 4 = -2$ This is not true.

D. $(3, -2)$ $y = -2x + 4 \rightarrow -2 = -2(3) + 4 = -2$ This is true!

40) Choice C is correct

Use simple interest formula: $I = prt$ ($I = interest, p = principal, r = rate, t = time$)

$I = (9,000)(0.045)(5) = 2,025$

STAAR Mathematics Practice Test 2

Answers and Explanations

1) Choice D is correct

The capacity of a red box is 20% bigger than the capacity of a blue box and it can hold 30 books. Therefore, we want to find a number that 20% bigger than that number is 30. Let x be that number. Then: $1.20 \times x = 30$, Divide both sides of the equation by 1.2. Then: $x = \frac{30}{1.20} = 25$

2) Choice C is correct

The smallest number is -15. To find the largest possible value of one of the other five integers, we need to choose the smallest possible integers for four of them. Let x be the largest number. Then: $-70 = (-15) + (-14) + (-13) + (-12) + (-11) + x \rightarrow -70 = -65 + x$

$$\rightarrow x = -70 + 65 = -5$$

3) The answer is: -122

Use PEMDAS (order of operation):

$[6 \times (-24) + 8] - (-4) + [4 \times 5] \div 2 = [-144 + 8] - (-4) + [20] \div 2 =$

$[-144 + 8] - (-4) + 10 = [-136] - (-4) + 10 = [-136] + 4 + 10 = -122$

4) Choice D is correct

Use FOIL method. $(2x + 2y)(2x - y) = 4x^2 - 2xy + 4xy - 2y^2 = 4x^2 + 2xy - 2y^2$

5) Choice D is correct

To solve absolute values equations, write two equations. $x - 10$ could be positive 3, or negative 3. Therefore, $x - 10 = 3 \Rightarrow x = 13$. $x - 10 = -3 \Rightarrow x = 7$.

Find the product of solutions: $7 \times 13 = 91$

6) Choice B is correct

The equation of a line in slope intercept form is: $y = mx + b$. Solve for y.

$4x - 2y = 12 \Rightarrow -2y = 12 - 4x \Rightarrow y = (12 - 4x) \div (-2) \Rightarrow y = 2x - 6$. The slope of this line is 2. The product of the slopes of two perpendicular lines is -1. Therefore, the slope of a line that is perpendicular to this line is: $m_1 \times m_2 = -1 \Rightarrow 2 \times m_2 = -1 \Rightarrow m_2 = \frac{-1}{2} = -\frac{1}{2}$

7) Choice A is correct

Plug in the value of x and y. $x = 3$ and $y = -2$

$$5(x + 2y) + (2 - x)^2 = 5(3 + 2(-2)) + (2 - 3)^2 = 5(3 - 4) + (-1)^2 = -5 + 1 = -4$$

8) Choice D is correct

The distance between Bob and Mike is 12 miles. Bob running at 6.5 miles per hour and Mike is running at the speed of 8 miles per hour. Therefore, every hour the distance is 1.5 miles less. $12 \div 1.5 = 8$

9) Choice D is correct

The failing rate is 11 out of 44 or $\frac{11}{44}$. Change the fraction to percent: $\frac{11}{44} \times 100\% = 25\%$

25 percent of students failed. Therefore, 75 percent of students passed the exam.

10) Choice D is correct

Solve for x. $-1 \le 2x - 3 < 1 \Rightarrow$ (add 3 all sides) $-1 + 3 \le 2x - 3 + 3 < 1 + 3 \Rightarrow$

$2 \le 2x < 4 \Rightarrow$ (divide all sides by 2) $1 \le x < 2$. x is between 1 and 2. Choice D represents this inequality.

11) The answer is 60.

Let x be the width of the rectangle. Use Pythagorean Theorem: $a^2 + b^2 = c^2$

$x^2 + 5^2 = 13^2 \Rightarrow x^2 + 25 = 169 \Rightarrow x^2 = 169 - 25 = 144 \Rightarrow x = 12$

Area of the rectangle $= length \times width = 5 \times 12 = 60$

12) Choice B is correct

The perimeter of the trapezoid is $36\ cm$. Therefore, the missing side (height) is

$40 - 8 - 12 - 6 = 14$. Area of a trapezoid: $A = \frac{1}{2} h (b_1 + b_2) = \frac{1}{2}(14)(6 + 8) = 98$

13) Choice B is correct

The probability of choosing a Club is $\frac{13}{52} = \frac{1}{4}$

14) Choice B is correct

$$average\ (mean) = \frac{sum\ of\ terms}{number\ of\ terms} \Rightarrow 80 = \frac{sum\ of\ terms}{50} \Rightarrow sum = 80 \times 50 = 4,000$$

The difference of 94 and 69 is 25. Therefore, 25 should be subtracted from the sum.

$$4000 - 25 = 3{,}975. \ mean = \frac{sum\ of\ terms}{number\ of\ terms} \Rightarrow mean = \frac{3{,}975}{50} = 79.5$$

15) Choice B is correct

To get a sum of 6 for two dice, we can receive $(1,5), (5,1), (2,4), (4,2), (3,3)$. So, we have 5 options. To get a sum of 9, we can receive $(6,3), (3,6), (4,5), (5,4)$. So, we have 4 options. Since, we have $6 \times 6 = 36$ total options, the probability of getting a sum of 6 and 9 is 9 $(4 + 5)$ out of 36 or $\dfrac{9}{36} = \dfrac{1}{4}$

16) The answer is 10.

Use formula of rectangle prism volume. $V = (length)(width)(height) \Rightarrow$

$$2500 = (25)(10)(height) \Rightarrow height = 2{,}500 \div 250 = 10$$

17) Choice C is correct

To find the number of possible outfit combinations, multiply number of options for each factor:

$3 \times 5 \times 6 = 90$

18) Choice C is correct

$4 \div \dfrac{1}{3} = 12$

19) Choice A is correct

The diagonal of the square is 4. Let x be the side. Use Pythagorean Theorem: $a^2 + b^2 = c^2$

$x^2 + x^2 = 4^2 \Rightarrow 2x^2 = 4^2 \Rightarrow 2x^2 = 16 \Rightarrow x^2 = 8 \Rightarrow x = \sqrt{8}$

The area of the square is: $\sqrt{8} \times \sqrt{8} = 8$

20) Choice C is correct

$$\text{Probability} = \frac{number\ of\ desired\ outcomes}{number\ of\ total\ outcomes} = \frac{10}{15 + 10 + 10 + 25} = \frac{10}{60} = \frac{1}{6}$$

21) Choice A is correct

Volume of the cube is less than 64 m^3. Use the formula of volume of cubes.

$volume = (one\ side)^3 \Rightarrow 64 > \Rightarrow 64 > (one\ side)^3$. Find the cube root of both sides. Then: $4 > one\ side$. The side of the cube is less than 4. Only choice A is less than 4.

22) Choice A is correct

The width of the rectangle is twice its length. Let x be the length. Then, $width = 2x$

Perimeter of the rectangle is 2 $(width + length) = 2(2x + x) = 72 \Rightarrow 6x = 72 \Rightarrow$

$x = 12$. Length of the rectangle is 12 meters.

23) Choice D is correct

average $= \dfrac{\text{sum of terms}}{\text{number of terms}} \Rightarrow$ (average of 6 numbers) $10 = \dfrac{\text{sum of numbers}}{6} \Rightarrow$ sum of 6 numbers is $10 \times 6 = 60$

(average of 4 numbers) $7 = \dfrac{\text{sum of numbers}}{4} \Rightarrow$ sum of 4 numbers is $7 \times 4 = 28$

$sum\ of\ 6\ numbers - sum\ of\ 4\ numbers = sum\ of\ 2\ numbers$

$60 - 28 = 32.$ Average of 2 numbers $= \dfrac{32}{2} = 16$

24) Choice C is correct

Solving Systems of Equations by Elimination

Multiply the first equation by (-2), then add it to the second equation.

$\begin{array}{l} -2(2x + 5y = 11) \\ \underline{4x - 2y = -26} \end{array} \Rightarrow \begin{array}{l} -4x - 10y = -22 \\ 4x - 2y = -26 \end{array} \Rightarrow -12y = -48 \Rightarrow y = 4$

Plug in the value of y into one of the equations and solve for x.

$2x + 5(4) = 11 \Rightarrow 2x + 20 = 11 \Rightarrow 2x = -9 \Rightarrow x = -4.5$

25) Choice D is correct

Area of the circle is less than $81\pi\ ft^2$. Use the formula of areas of circles. $Area = \pi r^2 \Rightarrow 81\pi > \pi r^2 \Rightarrow 81 > r^2 \Rightarrow r < 9$. Radius of the circle is less than $9\ ft$. Therefore, the diameter of the circle is less than $18\ ft$. Only choice D is less than $18 ft$.

26) Choice D is correct

Th ratio of boy to girls is $4 : 7$. Therefore, there are 4 boys out of 11 students. To find the answer, first divide the total number of students by 11, then multiply the result by 4. $55 \div 11 = 5 \Rightarrow 5 \times 4 = 20$. There are 20 boys and 35 $(55 - 20)$ girls. So, 15 more boys should be enrolled to make the ratio $1 : 1$

27) Choice A is correct

Let x be the number of new shoes the team can purchase. Therefore, the team can purchase $120\ x$. The team had $20,000 and spent $10000. Now the team can spend on new shoes $10,000 at most. Now, write the inequality: $120x + 10,000 \leq 20,000$

28) The answer is 35.

Jason needs an 70% average to pass for five exams. Therefore, the sum of 5 exams must be at lease $5 \times 70 = 350$. The sum of 4 exams is: $68 + 72 + 85 + 90 = 315$.

The minimum score Jason can earn on his fifth and final test to pass is: $350 - 315 = 35$

29) Choice B is correct

Isolate and solve for x. $\frac{2}{3}x + \frac{1}{6} = \frac{1}{2} \Rightarrow \frac{2}{3}x = \frac{1}{2} - \frac{1}{6} = \frac{1}{3} \Rightarrow \frac{2}{3}x = \frac{1}{3}$

Multiply both sides by the reciprocal of the coefficient of x. $(\frac{3}{2})\frac{2}{3}x = \frac{1}{3}(\frac{3}{2}) \Rightarrow x = \frac{3}{6} = \frac{1}{2}$

30) Choice B is correct

Use simple interest formula: $I = prt$ (I = interest, p = principal, r = rate, t = time)

$I = (14000)(0.035)(2) = 980$

31) Choice D is correct

Simplify. $5x^2y^3(2x^2y)^3 = 5x^2y^3(8x^6y^3) = 40x^8y^6$

32) Choice C is correct

Surface Area of a cylinder $= 2\pi r\,(r + h)$, the radius of the cylinder is 2 ($4 \div 2$) inches and its height is 8 inches. Therefore, Surface Area of a cylinder $= 2\pi\,(2)\,(2 + 8) = 40\,\pi$

33) Choice D is correct

First, find the sum of four numbers. average $= \frac{\text{sum of terms}}{\text{number of terms}} \Rightarrow 48 = \frac{\text{sum of 4 numbers}}{4} \Rightarrow$ sum of 4 numbers $= 48 \times 4 = 192$. The sum of 4 numbers is 192. If a fifth number that is greater than 65 is added to these numbers, then the sum of 5 numbers must be greater than $192 + 65 = 257$. If the number was 65, then the average of the numbers is:

average $= \frac{256}{5} = 51.4$. Since the number is bigger than 65. Then, the average of five numbers must be greater than 51.4. Choice D is greater than 51.4

34) The answer is 130.

Use the information provided in the question to draw the shape.

Use Pythagorean Theorem: $a^2 + b^2 = c^2$

$50^2 + 120^2 = c^2 \Rightarrow 2500 + 14400 = c^2 \Rightarrow 16900 = c^2 \Rightarrow c = 130$

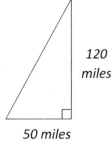

120 miles

50 miles

35) Choice D is correct

Plug in 140 for F and then solve for C. $C = \frac{5}{9}(F - 32) \Rightarrow C = \frac{5}{9}(140 - 32) \Rightarrow$

$C = \frac{5}{9}(108) = 60$

36) Choice A is correct

First, find the number. Let x be the number. Write the equation and solve for x. 150% of a number is 75, then: $1.5 \times x = 75 \Rightarrow x = 75 \div 1.5 = 50$. 80% of 50 is: $0.8 \times 50 = 40$

37) Choice A is correct

Simplify and combine like terms. $(5x^3 - 8x^2 + 2x^4) - (4x^2 - 2x^4 + 2x^3) \Rightarrow$
$(5x^3 - 8x^2 + 2x^4) - 4x^2 + 2x^4 - 2x^3 \Rightarrow 4x^4 + 3x^3 - 12x^2$

38) Choice B is correct

the population is increased by 10% and 20%. 10% increase changes the population to 110% of original population. For the second increase, multiply the result by 120%.

$(1.10) \times (1.20) = 1.32 = 132\%$. 32 percent of the population is increased after two years.

39) Choice C is correct

Three times of 25,000 is 75,000. One sixth of them cancelled their tickets.

One sixth of 75,000 equals 12,500 ($\frac{1}{6} \times 72,000 = 12,500$). 62,500 ($75,000 - 12,500 =$ 62,500) fans are attending this week

40) Choice B is correct.

A linear equation is a relationship between two variables, x and y, and can be written in the form of $y = mx + b$. A non-proportional linear relationship takes on the form $y = mx + b$, where $b \neq 0$ and its graph is a line that does not cross through the origin. Only in graph B, the line does not pass through the origin

"Effortless Math Education" Publications

Effortless Math authors' team strives to prepare and publish the best quality STAAR Grade 8 Mathematics learning resources to make learning Math easier for all. We hope that our publications help you learn Math in an effective way and prepare for the STAAR Grade 8 test.

We all in Effortless Math wish you good luck and successful studies!

Effortless Math Authors

www.EffortlessMath.com

... So Much More Online!

- ✓ FREE Math lessons

- ✓ More Math learning books!

- ✓ Mathematics Worksheets

- ✓ Online Math Tutors

Need a PDF version of this book?

Visit www.EffortlessMath.com

Visit www.EffortlessMath.com

for Online Math Practice

Made in the USA
Coppell, TX
07 January 2021